ANGELS AND DIRTY FACES

Also by Eric C. Bartholomew

Fiction
Distant Horizons

To CHRISTINE

6/8/11

ANGELS
AND
DIRTY FACES

BEST WISHES

Eric C. Bartholomew

First published in the United Kingdom in 2009
by KavanaghTipping Publishing,
www.kavanaghtipping.com

ISBN 978-1-906546-06-9

For Nan and Grumps

Preface

This book concentrates on the mid-fifties up to 1957. That time frame epitomizes my childhood, encapsulating an eclectic mix of everything I feel and remember about it.

Proud to be British was the feeling of the age. The map of the world, triumphantly displayed on school walls, was still two-thirds pink, the Empire the standard of the day. In 1953, our ingenuity, resourcefulness and adventurous spirit had been demonstrated afresh – we conquered Everest – and the young Queen Elizabeth II was newly on the throne.

An evening's entertainment would see everyone clustered around the wireless (radio) which stood where the television would be these days. There was a new feeling of moving away from the war years, especially for young people, and things were changing fast. Bill Haley and the Comets played Rock Around the Clock in the groundbreaking film *Blackboard Jungle* (you had to be twenty-one to see it), and Elvis the Pelvis, wiggling his hips on stage, was getting the young ones dancing and disgusting the old.

All this went on around the nucleus of our family, but it did not affect our daily lives. Our family clung to the old values of war time austerity. The slogans of the war years – *make do and mend; dig for victory* – were still ingrained in our family ethos. We had no money, but family values were strong beyond measure.

NB: Several names have been changed to protect the privacy of individuals.

Mum

Coming home from school in the summer of 1954, June and I turned into our road – Nursery Close, Walthamstow E17 – and saw a crowd further up the hill outside our house. Curiosity getting the better of us, we held hands and ran towards it.

'Careful June, don't fall over. I don't want to have to explain to Mum if you scrape your hands and knees.' Although, at nine, I was only a year older than my sister, I always felt responsible for her.

We wove our way through the people, right to the front.

'Why are these people standing outside our house, Eric?'

'Don't know, June.'

Looking up, I could see all our neighbours staring at us and then back to our shared tenement building. Their eyes looked gentle and yet somehow sad. Parked right in front of the building was a creamy white van with a silver bell on top.

'Let's go in,' I said to June, keeping hold of her hand and stepping forward. Two women who lived just up the road grabbed our shoulders and pulled us towards them.

'Now, dears, you don't want to go up there at the moment,' one of them said kindly, holding onto us firmly. June began to cry.

'Now, now,' said our neighbour, 'don't cry, lovey, your dad's been sent for. It won't be long until he gets home. You wait with us.'

'What's wrong?' I looked up at them, tears and confusion taking over.

Shouts and anguished screams came from inside. I recognised Mum's voice coming from afar. June began to cry even harder, and I began to struggle. I nearly escaped from the neighbour's grasp. I struggled even harder as tears flowed down my cheeks, but my metal-studded shoes, scraping and sliding on the tarmac, prevented me from getting away. The woman holding me called to her husband.

'George, give me a hand, will you?'

'Righto,' said George, grabbing me, his strong hands enveloping my shoulders like a vice. He shook me violently into submission. 'Don't struggle, boy. You don't want to go up there at the moment.'

That was the second time that had been said to me. What was going on?

'Now do as Aunt Maude says and be quiet. Your father will be home presently.'

The front door was already ajar. A flicker of movement just inside caught my eye. Shock seared through my brain as two white-coated figures struggled out. The crowd went silent. The only noise was our mum screaming at the top of her voice. Struggling between the two men, she was all tied up like one of Grumps' chickens ready for Sunday dinner. The men grunted from the effort of holding her up and walking her to the van.

'Fucking bastards! Pigs!' she spat at them – words I had never heard her say before. 'Get your fucking hands off of me!'

The crowd gasped with shock at what they were hearing. Her eyes were bulging and her face was bright red. She tried to lash out but her arms and hands were bound too tightly. Not her legs and feet though. She began to kick out, the men dancing sideways as the struggle continued down the concrete path.

'Lay her down!' a strong voice commanded from behind the struggle. The two men threw her to the ground. Her violent movements meant that she hit the concrete quite hard. Her head, as it met the pavement, sounded like an apple hitting a hollow tree trunk.

For me, everything began to slow down. It felt as if I was not there: this was happening to someone else's mother, not mine. The third man opened a small black leather case, reached inside and produced something large and silver with a glass middle. Reaching back into the bag again, he brought out a silver needle which he screwed into the cylinder. Once more his hand delved into the bag. Out came a small bottle, into which he pushed the needle. I noticed the veins on the backs of his hands throbbing. He tipped the bottle upside down and began to draw some of the liquid into the silver object, holding it up to the light. Satisfied, he removed the bottle, throwing it back into his bag. A squirt of liquid fell to the ground in a gentle arc.

All the time, Mum was struggling to be free. More awful swear words escaped from her mouth and her feet were kicking the pavement so violently that the heel from her left shoe broke off. As her legs pumped up and down, my most vivid memory is a small yellow stain on her white knickers. Everyone could see my mum's legs, white skin above her stockings exposed to the crowd right up to the top of her thighs. I felt embarrassed for her. She was usually so fussy.

'Hold her steady, I don't want this needle breaking in her arm. One of you lie across her legs, the other across her upper body.' The doctor looked hesitantly down at her. He couldn't stick the needle into her arms: they were all trussed up in the strait jacket. Moving between the men, he lifted one side of Mum's skirt, quickly jabbed the needle into her thigh and squeezed the plunger down. All the time, she was squirming and struggling. As he pulled the needle out, I could see her skin rising with it as if it didn't want to let the bloody thing go. Her movements began to lessen and her words began to slur, just like Dad's when he staggered home from work. This wasn't my mum. My mum cooked us dinners and tucked us up in bed at night.

Suddenly there was silence, apart from a few murmurings from the crowd. The two white-coated men stood up.

'Put her in the van.'

They picked Mum up between them. She was all limp now, her head lolling from side to side, her eyes rolled back into her head, her breathing heavy and laboured. I watched as spittle ran from the corner of her mouth.

'My mum! What are you doing with my mum?'

The doctor turned to look at Auntie Maude and George. 'Are these this woman's children?'

They nodded in reply.

'What's the matter with you people? How could you let them witness this?'

'Won't do 'em any harm,' protested George in their defence.

'You people!' exclaimed the doctor. 'I will never understand you in a million years.'

You people? Who was he talking about? My dad told me we were all God's children.

The doctor slammed the van's back doors, walked to the front of the vehicle and stepped into the passenger seat. 'Drive on quickly!' he ordered the driver.

The cream and white van screamed away, gears grinding, engine revving, bell ringing. I watched as it disappeared down the hill towards Oatland Rise. It blurred past the houses, a great bellow of diesel smoke following behind, turned the corner and disappeared. All that could be heard was the silver bell.

I looked down at June. She hadn't moved. There were no more tears, but she was ashen faced with shock. Just then a figure on a bicycle came careering round the top bend.

'Dad!' I cried. 'Dad!'

As he brought the bike to a screeching halt, he looked at the now disappearing crowd. 'What's up? I got a call at work telling me to hurry home. You kids all right?'

June just stood and stared.

Dad turned to Maud and George. 'Where's Joyce?'

'They've put her in a van and carted her off to the loony bin.'

Loony bin? Why my mum? I ran to Dad, trying to put my arms around him for comfort. June did not move.

'George!' Maude reprimanded. She looked embarrassed at George's bluntness as she went on to explain. 'They took her to Claybury.'

Claybury? Why my mum? She's not mad. Only the funny people go there.

Dad looked shocked. 'Can you have the kids

for a couple of hours?' He pushed me away, leaving me with my blinding tears.

''Course we can.'

Without looking at us, he cycled off in the same direction as the van.

'Come on, children,' said Aunt Maude, 'you come home with us.'

I grabbed June's hand and made a dash for our building; the front door was still open. June just dragged along behind me. We made the front door before Maude or George could grab us. Nobody was going to see us cry. I slammed the door shut behind us and leant back, listening.

'Get them kids out of there!' I could hear Maud screaming at George.

George strode down the path and banged violently on the door. 'Come out, you two! Come out here!'

I heard a passing neighbour shout back at him 'Leave 'em be, they've been through enough,' then George, grumbling as he walked back down the path, 'Charlie asked us to look after 'em. Come on Maude, let's go home. They won't come to any harm in there.'

I heard them walk away. June hadn't moved. She just stood there staring.

Dragging her upstairs, I pushed past our tenement neighbours, staring at us from each landing. Cigarettes drooped from several mouths; brightly coloured plastic curlers poked out from underneath garish multi-coloured scarves; mouths hung open and shocked eyeballs stared down at us. Others looked on with sorrowful gazes and several women tried to comfort us – great bosomy mounds crushing and consoling. I pushed away, still heading upstairs.

'Leave us alone,' I told them. 'I think you should go to bed,' I said manfully, taking June into

6

our attic room. I made her sit on the bed and took off her shoes. Next, I pulled back the covers. 'Come on, June, crawl in, be a good girl.'

She didn't protest. She lay her head on the pillow, her lush, chestnut-coloured hair surrounding her. 'Is Mum coming home?'

''Course she is,' I said, without knowing if this was true or not.

She popped her thumb into her mouth as I covered her up. She didn't make a sound as I tucked her up tightly. Her eyelids slowly closed and merciful sleep whisked her away. I tiptoed away from the bed towards the cold, one bar fire. A loud clunk echoed around the room as I switched it on. June did not stir.

I could hear the grandmother clock ticking down below, and the neighbours talking. I couldn't hold back any more. Silent sobs racked my body, the glowing fire the only warm thing in my life. I didn't feel hunger or anger, only numbness. The sight of our mum shrieking and screaming was going round and round in my head.

Some time later the shilling in the meter ran out: with a loud clunk, the meter had swallowed it. The warmth from my only comfort had died and I was sitting by the dead fire in the dark. The room returned to a black, icy feeling. I had nowhere to go.

Dad came home many hours later. I heard his boots on the bare wooden stairs and recognised his footsteps as he wearied his way up. Closing the door, he called gently for me.

'I'm here, Dad.'

'Why are you sitting in the dark?'

'Shilling's gone, Dad.'

He fumbled his way to the meter. I heard the scrape of the shilling as he turned the metal handle. The fire glowed once more.

I did not look up at him … just kept staring into the fire. 'What's up with Mum?' leapt out of my mouth.

He came and sat down the other side of the fire, and stayed there for several minutes, just staring. 'The doctors want to keep her in hospital for a little while. They said they'd have to do some tests. I've got to go back tomorrow evening.'

'Has something broke in Mum's head, Dad?'

'Well, yes son, something like that. I need you to help with June for the next few weeks.'

'OK, Dad.'

'Off you go to bed, son.'

I left him just staring at the one bar fire. I crawled, exhausted and fully clothed, into our bed and cried myself silently to sleep. 'Please get well, Mum, please.'

Nan

In the future our mum often went away for a few days or a few weeks. We never knew when or why it was going to happen, and it became normal to us kids. We were shunted off to our Nan's, which was great: it meant we skipped school. While all the other kids were at their desks, we were playing 'hide and seek' or 'cowboys and Indians' over the bomb sites. June was always the Indian so I could shoot her; she never seemed to mind. During our younger years we had more playtime than schooling and all the kids were envious of us.

When Mum came home she virtually lived down at Nan's, in Brook Road, the other end of Walthamstow, only going home when our dad came back from work. This meant June and I walking about a mile up Coppermill Lane to James Street station, and hopping on a train for two or three stops to Wood Street. According to the times of the trains, or us two messing about, we often missed the first train after school. Nobody seemed to mind. The whole trip varied between sixty and ninety minutes and we were always hungry when we reached Nan's.

When Dad got home from work, Nan fed him to the brim and, eventually, with June nodding off, we would set off for home. If we were unlucky, fog would descend, engulfing the whole of London and the surrounding area. Sometimes this turned into a 'pea souper' – smog; you couldn't see a hand in front of you. When this happened it was my job to walk in front of Dad's Norton motor bike and side car, shining a torch at the kerb side. It was hard to breathe in this laden air that consisted of trapped warm air mixed with coal and wood smoke from steam trains, houses and factory chimneys, plus any other noxious substance that might be belching out. The air looked yellowish grey, felt damp and tasted of the grime of London. I had to walk at a measured pace so my dad could keep up with me; the bike stayed in low gear the whole way home. It was a journey of about three or four miles, but in the 'pea souper' it became a nightmare marathon of two or three hours.

My whole childhood was spent in Walthamstow. Buses ran down Shernhall Street, going from the High Street to the Bakers Arms, Leyton and beyond – too far for us to imagine. Tramcars were still running and woe betide you if your bike wheel got caught in the tram lines: you knew you were coming off, and the cobble stones made the fall even harder.

In those days of the mid-fifties, church bells rang out, steam trains hooted, their coal dust permeating the air, school gates were left open, the smell of school dinners filling the air, and children played innocently. There was not much traffic and the streets and roads were narrow, so we kids could also play in the street with impunity – no Green Cross Code, no 'mind the traffic'. We knew a 'townie's' freedom: kids on roller skates tore up and down the middle of the road, girls played hopscotch on the pavement, or skipped with their skipping ropes – *one potato, two potatoes, three potatoes, four* – and we all played over the bomb sites. As we got older, the game might be 'doctors and nurses' with the older girls.

10

Talk about 'Cupid's balls'! How many times did I walk home with a 'stiffy' and my balls aching? What a frustrating time!

Street lighting was sparse and there were not many curtains in our neighbourhood then. Therefore, when inky blackness descended around us, bare light bulbs shone out into the street and people's evening pursuits were on display for passers by: dads might be helping sons with their Meccano building; mums might be helping daughters with sewing or knitting; other people might be sitting quietly reading. Some could not afford the electricity and they just stared into glowing open fires until it was time for bed.

Although none of this was the lifestyle of *our* family, we knew no envy. We considered ourselves luckier than most because what we could not get from Mum and Dad we got from Nan and Grumps.

There was virtually no crime, but then we were a poor neighbourhood and nobody had anything worth pinching – the pride and joy of a valve radio might be the only consumer presence in the household. It was always lino and no carpet, hand-me-down furniture, and beds that had slept generations – great high things, always about three foot six off the ground. The air and dampness from the air bricks ran from front to back of the house, travelling under the bed and making it too damp to sleep under there; you'd catch your death of cold. Nan's bed was our comfort and refuge, and where Nan and Grumps slept while we stayed with them I never knew or questioned.

Families like ours did not have fridges or washing machines and Monday was everyone's washing day, including Nan's. She scrubbed away the dirt with lye soap, wearing her fingers to the bone on the washboard, her hair tied up with a piece of white cloth. Many a time I saw damp, tousled locks being tucked back into place as heavy cauldrons of boiling clothes steamed up the whole kitchen. Reams of washing hung in all the back yards, billowing out in the wind, majestic galleons of blankets and sheets going nowhere.

Nan's week was governed by routine. Every afternoon she went out and did her cleaning jobs, as if she didn't have enough to do at home. Everyone in our situation penny-pinched. As my Grumps often repeated, needs must as the devil drives. Tuesday was baking day, and so the week went on, the routine eventually rolling all the weeks into one.

Like everyone else, Nan kept chickens and hens. They were a necessity but also the bane of her life. They clucked and crowed the presence of dawn, when Nan knew it was time to get up and rekindle the fires. The range, dampened down the night before, would be poked and prodded into life ready for the morning brew. Toasting forks were clean and waiting for the fire to glow so that we could toast the home made bread or tea cakes – nearly everything was homemade – and we were lucky if we got meat once or twice a week. No one was fat, but Nan was larger than life, puffing herself up with pride, anger and the struggle of feeding and tending her flock.

She stood five foot nothing in her wrinkled stockings, which were sometimes rolled down to her ankles and resting on her slippers. She had several pinnies, every one the same colour and pattern, and her hair was forever in curlers, covered over with a brightly coloured scarf. Her eyes, a piercing cobalt blue, had a softness to them. They looked as if they'd seen the world forever. If she managed to catch you for a cuddle, which she did often because she loved to cuddle us, you took a deep breath before entering the

12

realms of her great bosom; otherwise you would die of asphyxiation. That bosom tried to escape through her blouse every time she spoke, gesticulating with her immense arms and sausage fingers. She never swore and although she could snore the house down, her voice was surprisingly gentle. She had sayings which I did not understand at the time: *A stitch in time saved many a man from embarrassing himself, I can tell you ... Put the wood in the hole, it's draughty ... The way to a man's heart is through his beer and his belly.* She always winked conspiratorially.

She was the boss, although Grumps would never admit this, and she'd been engaged eight times before capturing him. She didn't mind, she said, because she'd kept all the engagement rings 'for a rainy day'. As it seemed to pour every week in our house, they didn't last long. I think the pawn brokers or the 'tally' man got the lot.

When she went out, off came the curlers, revealing a head of tightly curled hair; off came the pinny, and on went the rabbit skin coat she wore to the pub. Half a yard of lipstick covered her ample lips, and two pounds of polyfilla filled in the cracks on her face. 'Come on Albert, we're having a night on the tiles,' she would say, but she didn't smile in case the polyfilla fell off. Her favourite tipple was gin and orange, all night long, and she always came home with a bag full of pub glasses. We needed them for our many parties.

She left me a legacy of love that still binds me today. On her death the family fractured: there was nobody strong enough to pick up the mantle. My heart still bleeds from an open wound. She was our Nan and mum all in one. I can still see her standing silhouetted in the doorway to life. When she died I knew I would miss her forever.

Moonlighting

Our lives altered when we moved in with Nan and Grumps. What started off as a few days ended up stretching to a full year.

'Come on, son, wake up.'

I rubbed my eyes and propped myself up on one elbow, trying not to disturb the overcoats covering us, determined to keep the hard won warmth from escaping from our two bodies. Bleary eyed, I turned my head to June, bundled up next to me, almost buried under the coats. Her lips were slightly puckered in sleep, her eyelids fluttering.

Dad put a hand on my shoulder. 'Come on, son, your sister too.' He absently brushed his dark hair away from his eyes.

I could hear Mum in the background, grunting as she pulled our heavy suitcase towards the door, trying not to disturb the floorboards. I could just make out Dad's figure, ghost-like in the moonlight, silhouetted by far away street lamps and made even more eerie by the stream of chilled breath billowing from his mouth. The cold bit at my cheeks as I turned once more to shake June.

'What is it?' She moaned herself awake, rubbing her eyes. 'Mum!' she said in a panic. 'My eyes are stuck! I can't open them!' Her little voice rose with fear and Mum quickly placed her hand over my sister's mouth.

'We can't do anything about it now. Just be quiet!' she hissed.

The discharge from June's eyes had sealed them shut. I looked over at her. So much had been secreted as to completely cover her sockets. She looked like a beautiful doll with no eyes.

'Dad says we've got to wake up.'

'It's so cold.' She clutched the winter coats around her and sat, unseeing, at the bottom of the bed.

'Ready, Charlie?' From the far side of the room came Mum's whispered screech through her cupped hand.

'Wait a minute, Joyce.' He dragged us from the bed. 'Now don't make any noise, kids.'

June, still half asleep and with one sock inside out, fumbled with her cardy, doing her buttons up wrongly. In the half light she also managed to put her shoes on the wrong feet, but tying the laces was out of the question. She tried to balance herself, fumbling in her temporary blindness.

'Silly girl, look at you,' Dad whispered. He ruffled her hair good-humouredly as he helped her.

'Come on Charlie, for Christ's sake!' Mum hissed under her breath. 'Get a bloody move on will you!' Panic was just under the surface.

'Ok Joyce, keep your hair on. Don't get your knickers in a twist.'

Now I knew why we'd gone to bed half-dressed. Here we go again: no money for the rent. Looking around the darkened room, I said goodbye to what had been home for the last six months: the one bar fire, trying manfully to heat this loft room; the one bare bulb, our only source of light; the big double bed dominating the room, and the only place to get warm;

16

the brown-stained butler sink, one brass cold water tap constantly dripping; the little gas cooker next to the little four-seater table; the bob-a-time gas meter on the wall; the bare floorboards that creaked when you moved; the peeling, green-distempered walls; the large skylight that sucked all the heat from the room. On the second landing downstairs was one toilet, shared by all on the upper landing. All this for five bob a week – and now they couldn't even manage that. Where would we end up this time? Dad never seemed to settle. His gipsy blood kept him on the move; only Mum seemed to stop him wandering off both physically and mentally. Not that we had much choice this time.

Grabbing the coats off the bed, Dad put one of the blanket-coats on and threw the other one to Mum. Unfurling our makeshift pillows, he helped us into our pillow-coats. Mum grabbed June under her arm and half carried, half dragged her towards the darkened doorway.

'Now, be quiet!' Mum threatened.

June knew better than to cry. At eight years old she was aware of the tension around her. I felt very protective towards her: born on my first birthday, she had been a present from Mum and Dad.

Dad placed his hand tentatively on the round brass handle, turned it slowly, eased the door upwards to stop it squeaking, pulled it slightly open and peered down the dark cavernous staircase. All was silent below. He looked round at us and gestured with his finger to his lips. Opening the door wider, he listened to the silence broken only by the ticking of the great clock in the hallway below. Standing at the end of the landing, he beckoned us to follow, his cloth cap on his head, his boots with leather laces tied together, hanging round his neck. He disappeared down the dark staircase, the heavy, scuffed leather suitcase held out in front of him. I followed, shoes in hand, Mum next, carrying June. Third landing: breathing nervously, we listened again to the silence. Second landing: my ears, nose and fingers were numb with cold. I looked back. Mum was still right behind me, June staring with sightless eyes. First landing: only the remaining staircase to go. The front door was illuminated by the street lights.

Dad had one foot in the air, his other foot on the first tread when an almighty din ripped throughout the hall. We all jumped. My cold fingers had released my shoes; the noise as they tumbled down the stairs was exaggerated in the stillness. To make matters worse, the grandmother clock underneath the landing staircase then struck four. Dad looked at me, his glaring eyes telling me he wished I had never been born. Nobody moved. We didn't even dare breathe. Nothing happened. No door opened. No shouts of 'runners!' – nothing.

Cautiously descending to the front door, my heart pounded as I tiptoed across the cold Victorian floor, the tiles numbing the soles of my feet, and retrieved my shoes. I could feel my father's glare piercing the back of my neck. He turned the large brass key. The top and bottom bolts scraped back reluctantly. The old grandmother clock ticked loudly and the wait seemed endless. At last the door opened and the cold night air rushed in, hitting us with a vengeance. Slipping through, we made our escape. It was Christmas Eve – no time to be homeless. But Dad would see us all right. Moonlighting was just another way of life for us. As long as we were together, Dad would find a way.

By Christmas Eve afternoon we were sitting round the open fire in Nan and Grumps' scullery. Grumps was poking the open fire with one hand, a toasting fork in the other, as he looked down at me squatting on the stone hearth. 'Don't get too close. If you burn your clothes they'll be on my ear.' He scuffed my hair with his outstretched hand, smiling kindly. A home-made fag dangled from his lips; brown tobacco juice mingled with saliva and ran down it, extinguishing the smouldering end. Mum and Dad were in the small kitchen, arguing with Nan, not realising that Grumps and I could hear every angry word.

'You can stay here over Christmas, but you've got to find somewhere for yourselves. You can't keep coming back here.'

'Where can we go, Mum?' The panic in my mother's voice was still evident from our earlier escape.

Voices were raised in anger.

'You married her, Charlie! It's up to you. You're the breadwinner!'

'Don't you think I've tried? Ever since I came out of the RAF, you know I have.'

'You shouldn't have had the kids then. With nowhere to live, what possessed you?'

'Here we go again! Every time!'

I heard Dad hit the wall in temper, and I could hear Mum crying. The smell of old greens and roast potatoes mixed with anger. Grumps raised his eyebrows, hand on my shoulder. The fire crackled in front of me, turning my knees blotchy.

'Move back, boy. You'll get chillblains on your knees.' We both laughed. 'Young people today don't know they're born. In my day ...'

Dad came through the kitchen door. 'What you bleedin' laughin' at?'

My smile died on my face.

Grumps looked up. 'Come on Charlie, it's Christmas. Think of the little 'uns.'

'Where's June?' Dad looked at me.

'Mum bathed her eyes and she's gone out in the garden. She's still crying.'

'I bet she's in the chicken coop again.'

Clara the bantam entered the scullery and pecked her way towards the fire. Dad kicked out.

'Bloody thing. Why d'yer let it in the 'ouse?'

'This is my 'ouse and I'll do what I like, see!' Grumps rose out of his rocking chair, his face scarlet with rage. The whole family was never far from instant anger.

Nan, hearing the scraping of chairs, raised voices and Clara clucking, rushed in like a pocket battleship, ladle in hand, curlers escaping from under her hastily tied scarf, to stand there built like a brick shed. 'Now then, now then! What's all this?'

Clara left a deposit on the lino.

Grumps sat down again, staring defiantly at Nan. 'Why d'yer name that bloody bird? If you 'adn't it would've been in the pot by now.'

He went back to his favourite hobby, staring into the fire. Dad disappeared back into the kitchen. I sat there motionless. If I stayed still nobody could see me. Nan shoved Clara out and June stayed in the chicken coop.

The front door opened and slammed shut again. There was a shuffle down the corridor and the door of the back room opened.

'Hello Bob,' Grumps greeted his youngest child and only son. (Woe betide anyone who called him Bobby; Grumps wouldn't have it.) Bob was some twenty years younger than my mum, his sister, and only one month older than me. Bob, eleven years old, going on forty-two, never a child, couldn't wait to grow up. He spoke proper, not like us. Don't know where he got it from. He was Nan and Grumps' pride and joy.

'Hello Eric.'

'Hello Bob, where have you been?'

'Out on my bike.'

Lucky Devil. Ears, nose and knees bright red with cold.

'Coming out to play?'

'Not 'arf. Where's your bike?'

'Outside.' He pointed to a three-wheeled Raleigh with fixed chrome brakes. Magic! Sometimes he would let me ride piggyback, feet planted firmly astride the axle between the two back wheels. Off we would go. He would never let me drive, so I would have my revenge: I would dribble down his back or if it was cold enough, I'd snot him on his greasy head.

We pedalled furiously down the road. There was only one car parked in the whole street. What did Bob do? He ran smack bang straight into it! Over the top of his head I went, doing my impression of Superman until – crack! The sound of my head hitting the car's back window was followed by arms, knees and body sliding down the boot, with the bumper intervening on the way. My poor knees thumped onward and downward. Thank God for Bob, lying on his side, clutching the handle bars and still pedalling furiously. My knee caught him squarely in the left eye. The other hit him in the back. A sort of groan left his mouth and he stopped pedalling. We both lay on the gravel, breathing hard.

'What happened? Who put that car there?'

'Mr Barclay – yesterday!' I said sarcastically. 'What do you mean, who put it there, you idiot? How do I know?'

21

'I didn't see it. I was racing in the Isle of Man TT. Let's go before Mr Barclay comes out.'

Mr Barclay – Lord Snooty we called him – was only a bus driver but thought himself a cut above the general rabble of the street. The car itself was an old square Mayflower, black and greasy; whatever marks or scratches we left would just be added to the rest.

Picking ourselves up, we inspected the damage. Neither of us cried, not in front of each other, anyway. My knees were bruised and battered and the lump on my head was by now beginning to throb.

'I think we've been lucky,' Bob said, brushing his straight mousy hair out of his eyes. I didn't mention his eye would soon turn to hues of yellow and purple. He picked up the bike.

'Look,' he said, 'the front wheel's buckled. Dad's gonna kill me! What are we going to do?'

'Put it in the garden shed and maybe after Christmas we can get Mr Brent at number 42 to straighten it out. He's always tinkering with old bikes.'

'Good idea, Eric.' Bob locked his knees around the front wheel, feet placed firmly on either side, and straightened the handlebars, bringing them back in line with the battered front wheel. Then with each of us holding one side of the handlebars we lifted the front wheel off the ground, heaved the bike back onto the pavement, scurried home down the side alley and stashed the bike under some greasy old blankets in the back shed.

We walked down the concrete path, past the hens scratching away in their coop, past the cat cages, and past the rabbits in their hutches, each looking at us with one eye. They always seemed to be staring out of the side of their cages, eyes looking through the

22

chicken wire at the outside world, missing nothing, long ears pricked back on the lookout for Mr Foxy.

Grumps was standing at the back door holding a zinc bucket full of a mix of left over bacon rinds, old fat, potato, carrot and cabbage peelings: a glutinous mess, but like caviar to the chickens – good egg-laying fodder, as he put it. 'Blimey, what you been up to? You've been in the wars; what happened?'

Bob and I looked at each other. I stepped forward. 'Well Grumps, we've been in a fight with the Smiths in the next road.'

'Did you give as good as you got?' asked Grumps.

We both puffed our chests out. 'Of course we did.'

'Good. I'll have a few words with Mr Smith when I see him down the boozer on Saturday night.' He unconsciously curled his fist into a ball. My Grumps: he was well known for his short fuse.

We skipped round him and entered the kitchen, fighting each other to see who would go first to wash, grabbing hold of the brass cold water tap together. 'Me first, me first!' 'No, me!' 'No, me!'

The noise brought Nan into view. 'You two have been up to mischief again. Look at the pair of you! Bob, your eye!'

He lifted his hand to his face and winced. 'Blimey!'

'Don't swear! How many times have I got to tell you!' She cuffed the ear next to his good eye.

'Ow, Mum!'

'Well, if I catch you fighting again I'll box yer ears, do you hear me? Pull your socks up, the pair of you, tea's on the table. The family's coming round later and staying overnight for Christmas dinner tomorrow. Now wash up and come and eat.' She opened the kitchen door and shouted to Grumps. 'Albert, tea's on the table. Now, don't keep us all waiting.'

After washing ourselves, Bob and I tried to get through the parlour door at the same time.

'Boys, come and sit up at the table,' scolded Mum, already seated next to Dad. June had been prised from the chicken coop, washed and scrubbed till she shone, a little angel propped up on pillows in her chair next to Mum. Mum and Dad had already been filled in by Nan on our adventures. We scrambled up onto our chairs. Grumps appeared in the doorway, rubbing his hands on a tea towel.

"'Ow many times do I have to tell yer, Albert? Use the 'and towel, not the tea towel!' Nan remonstrated. 'Now who's to say grace?' She looked around the large wooden table.

'I will,' I said enthusiastically. I'd learnt a new prayer in the street. Billy Cole had taught me.

'Go on then,' prompted Nan.

We all placed our hands together and lowered our heads.

'Our Father what be in 'eaven, 'allowed be thy name. For what we are about to receive may the Lord make us truly thankful. Ashes to ashes, dust to dust, if your belly don't bust, your bum hole will. Amen.'

I lifted my head. Mum and Nan looked at me with horror on their faces. Grumps stuffed the tea towel into his mouth. Dad's head disappeared under the table looking for something. I grinned back.

'Gawd, luv a duck,' said Mum, 'where'd he get that one?'

'Not out of a Christmas cracker, that's for sure,' replied Nan.

Dad's head popped back up from under the table as Grumps took the tea towel from his mouth

24

and pretended to mop his brow. 'Dig in!' he said. 'A feast fit for a king!'

Set before us was home made bread and dripping, with margarine and blackcurrant jam or golden syrup. Nan's famous bread pudding covered with sugar was proudly presented on a tiered cake stand with a paper doily underneath. Stone glazed plates with aluminium knives and forks covered a bleached-white, starched-to-attention tablecloth. The fire crackled in the hearth behind us.

When my bum was warm and my belly full, I asked, 'Please Nan, can I get down from the table?'

'Not until everyone's finished.'

I sat there and waited. The front door knocker banged twice – the excuse I needed. 'I'll get it.' I jumped down before anyone could protest and ran through the parlour door and down the passage. I reached up and undid the door. 'Hello Uncle Jack and Auntie Vera.' With them was little Christine, only six years old, peering round her mum's skirts.

'Merry Christmas!' Uncle Jack pushed the front door open wide and they all trooped in. Auntie Vera pulled Jack back by the scruff of his overcoat.

'Wipe your feet, Jack. We don't want Mum moaning. Take your coat off and hang mine and Christine's up too.' Shaking the cold from her large frame, she waddled down the corridor.

Jack stood there, almost as tall as Auntie Vera was wide, shaking out the coats before reaching on tiptoe to hang them up. His bald head was gleaming – I always thought he rubbed it with furniture polish – and his beard was neatly trimmed. Why do bald men wear their hair on their chins, I wondered.

We went into the parlour, the new arrivals heading straight for the fire to warm themselves. Mum got up from the table to wish Vera a Merry

Christmas, acknowledging Jack and Christine over her sister's shoulder as she hugged her.

'Right,' said Nan after the greetings, 'let's clear the table. Make Christine up a plate of goodies. Jack, Vera, if you're 'ungry dig in now. Albert, don't just sit there, get everyone a drink will you?'

Grumps busied himself taking drinks orders – schooners of sherry, or Babycham for the ladies, beer for the men and Nan's home made lemonade or ginger beer for us kids. 'Boys, help yourselves and then help the young'uns. Then up to bed, it's going to be a long night.'

'But—' Bob and I protested.

'Don't 'but' me, do as you're told or Father Christmas won't come. Nan's banked the fire up in your bedroom for all of you. Up you go or I'll send the bogeyman to tuck you in.'

'Albert, stop frightening the nippers,' Nan scolded. 'Go on, up you go now, and I'll be up in a tick to tuck you in. Like quick! Shoo!'

We all four ran out of the room and up the stairs, June holding my hand tightly and Bob dragging little Christine upwards. The glow from the fire cast shadows on the top floor landing. We ran along the corridor together and through the open bedroom door. Bob and I let go of the girls' hands and dived onto the bed, the springs squeaking their protest, the brass headboard banging against the wall. Pulling the girls after us, we bounced around together, our shadows dancing around the room, the girls squeaking with delight.

'Cor! My knees still hurt,' I cried.

'I can hardly see out of my right eye,' Bob sniffed, cuffing a long snot on his pullover sleeve.

Nan came in a few minutes later. 'Right!' she said. 'Clothes off, pyjamas on. Boys, help the girls with

26

their nighties.' She took a cold flannel from behind her back and before we knew what was happening she had washed all our faces and hands.

'Nan!' we protested, goose bumps flaring.

'Now you lot, in you get! The sooner you get to sleep, the sooner Father Christmas will be here. Under you go.'

'Usual shift work, Nan?' I gave her a wry, sympathetic smile.

'Gawd bless you,' she smiled back.

There weren't enough beds to go round and I knew that Mum, Nan and Aunt Vera would be sleeping the twilight shift and then get up and give the bed to the men, who would sleep a few morning daylight hours after keeping themselves awake until dawn playing cards and sipping beer.

Nan fluffed the pillows and settled us down, tucking blankets around our ears. She stroked our heads one by one, all thoughts of what would happen after Christmas forgotten for the moment. 'Nighty night my little angels, sleep tight, God bless. Don't let the bed bugs bite.'

Bob was one side of the bed, me the other, the girls in between already entering the Land of Nod, June sucking her thumb, Christine slurping on her piece of cloth. Nan checked the fire, tiptoed across the bare floorboards and closed the door quietly.

'You asleep yet, Bob?'

No answer. I lifted my head slightly, turned and took a peek at him over the girls' heads. His eyes were staring at the ceiling. The fire, dampened down with coal dust and ash from the bottom of the grate should keep us warm all night. Occasionally a little piece of dust fell between the coals causing a spark to fly up the chimney. The spark's brightness danced across the ceiling, just for a second. Reds, pinks and ambers – all children knew these firelight fairies, sent on this special night to summon Santa.

'You asleep, Eric?'

I didn't answer. There was no way I was going to sleep before him.

Christmas Morning

'Are you awake, Bob?' I rubbed my eyes open. The room was cloaked in darkness.

'That you, Eric?'

'I just heard my dad leaving the room. Must've put our presents over the mantelpiece.

'What time is it, Bob?'

'Don't know. Time to open our presents.'

I could feel June tucked up beside me, her body warmth glowing on my thigh.

'Don't wake the girls; we'll just do ours.'

'Righto.'

We jumped out of bed, the dull light from the dampened down fire throwing a red glow around the room. With bare feet on creaking floorboards, we crept towards the stockings dangling from the fireplace. Quietly we removed the ones labelled for us. Untying the knotted string holding the Christmas parcels together, we tore open the colourful paper.

'What you got, Bob?'

'I think it's a Meccano set – just what I wanted. Good old Father Christmas. What you got, Eric?'

'A hand gun, just like the ones the cowboys use in Saturday morning pictures. Smashing!'

'I got a gun as well.'

'What sort?'

'A spud gun,' he replied. 'You know, the one where you push the gun's end into a potato, pull it out and you can shoot bits of spud at people.'

All the time, we knelt in front of the glowing fire, whispering excitedly.

'I'll swap my gun for yours. Please Bob!'

'Maybe,' he replied. 'Maybe, now and again. What else you got, Eric?'

'Me dad's made me ... I mean, *Father Christmas has brought me* a wood and elastic catapult.'

'Lucky you. Then we'll definitely swap.'

Reaching into the stockings we both removed a bag of bright coloured glass marbles, some large, some small; next, a packet of fivestones each. We'd played this game before, sitting in with those poncy uniformed kids from the grammar school down the road. I could never understand why they were called five*stones* when they were made of different coloured wood. The idea was to throw the small wooden ball that came with them into the air and scoop up as many 'stones' as possible, catching the ball with the same hand before it hit the ground. Easy. Then you'd throw the ball up once more, followed by the stones, and try to catch as many as possible on the back of your hand before the ball hit the ground. The one that could balance the most on the back of his hand was the winner. This was a bit trickier, but after many hours of practice, I had already become quite adept. Beating the grammar school ponces became my way of feeling better about myself.

'I can't wait to get out into the street with these,' I said. 'Billy Cole and old Wozzy will be screaming with envy.'

After that came packets of assorted sweets: jelly babies, flying saucers (sherbet inside coloured rice paper), Spanish wood you chewed for hours, liquorice all sorts, a sherbet dab and a packet of aniseed balls. I turned my nose up at the aniseed balls. I'd swap those at school for something else. I put them in the top pocket of my pyjamas and forgot about them.

'Cor, look at that!' Bob held out a large round sweet.

'A gobstopper,' I replied, reaching into my stocking looking for mine. My hand wrapped round it as Bob tried to force his into his mouth. I'd had one before and knew that once it went in you couldn't take it out for hours and had to mumble and suck. As it got smaller you could remove the offending sticky gobstopper, put it your pocket and forget it until you fancied another go, fluff and all.

We gathered up all the string and torn paper, stuffing it back into the stockings, rehanging them on the mantelpiece.

'Can't wait to try them out in the morning.'

'Me too,' I said as we scrambled back under the blankets, the girls still asleep. We cuddled up to them, my mind whizzing, thinking of climbing trees and shooting at birds with my catapult, playing cowboys and Indians, hiding behind the broken walls on the bombsite, shooting at each other. With these thoughts racing through my mind, my eyelids fluttered and I drifted into an innocent sleep.

Lifting my head off the pillow, I locked my eyes on the four large socks dangling from the fireplace, full to the brim with little coloured boxes. Now it was really Christmas. I glanced towards the window, where the curtains had been left open all night. 'Bob, it's snowing,'

He turned his head towards the frost covered glass. Large snowflakes drifted past. We smiled at each other in anticipation of the day to come. The smell of the roasting chickens was wafting up into our room; even so, ice had formed on the inside of the sash windows. I rubbed my eyes awake, smiling but with my tongue stuck to the roof of my mouth from all the licking and sticking of the day before, when it had been our job to make all the paper chains – greens, blues, reds, yellows, all the colours of the rainbow. My tongue felt like the bottom of a bird cage. My lips still felt blotchy from the paper glue.

'Are you awake, Bob?'

A mousy haired head appeared above the mound of the two girls sleeping between us.

'What's the time?' he asked rubbing his eyes.'

'Just turned septic by my wrist!' I said caustically. 'How do I know, it's light init?'

'Hello Eric,' June said sleepily.

Christine was turned turtle and her feet were still asleep on the pillow.

'It's Christmas!' I shouted excitedly.

Nan popped her head round the door. 'Quiet, now, your dads are asleep. No noise now.'

'Yes Nan,' we whispered.

Nan looked at the fireplace. 'Father Christmas been, I see.'

Bob and I looked sceptically back. 'Oh, has he really?'

June looked up in surprise, her great moon dish eyes shining excitedly in the dawn light. She jumped out of bed, her pink nightie swirling round her. 'Which one's mine?' she asked, clapping her hands with joy.

'Your name's pinned on it.'

June reached up, pulling her sock off the mantelpiece. The metal ornament holding it in place wobbled precariously and decided to nosedive off the mantelpiece, head first. It bounced off June's toes and a shocked scream left her open mouth. She began to jump up and down, her presents flying every which way. Tears rolled down her cheeks.

Nan grabbed her up into her ample bosom. 'There, there, girlie.' She swung her backwards and forwards, her great batwing arms enfolding June comfortingly. 'Let's have a look at your toes.'

'It hurts, Nan.' June sobbed as she gulped great lungfuls of air. Her nose began to run.

'There there,' soothed Nan, stroking her hair, 'let's kiss it better.' She raised June's foot up, examining the toes. 'Nothing's broken; it just looks a little sore. You'll mend.' Nan plonked June onto the bed. A muffled cry came from inside the bedcovers.

'Aw Nan, she's sitting on me 'ead.'

I stood up, pulling Christine's feet towards me.

''Morning Christine,' I said smiling.

'You woke me up,' she said, still sucking on her piece of cloth.

'Merry Christmas, Chris, Bob, June, Nan.'

June smiled through her tears. I loved my sister so much.

'Last one into the scullery's a sissy,' said Nan.

Bob and I burst from the bedroom at the same time, both rushing through the door and down the stairs. We could hear the girls squealing in protest. Halfway down the stairs my pyjamas came undone, heading down towards my ankles. I shouted in surprise, trying to grab the handrail and my willy at the same time, one hand over my privates, the other one missing the rail altogether. My legs became completely entangled and I dived down the stairs, landing head first and skinning my elbows and knees yet again as my legs rapped the last step of the staircase. Bob jumped the rest of the way, landing with a thump on my back.

33

'I'll get you later,' I screamed through my pain and wounded pride.

He laughed as he went through the door into the back room and entered the scullery at a run.

'Steady, lad, steady.' A bear-hug-cum-rugby-tackle lifted Bob off his feet as Nan stopped him in his tracks. 'Be careful!' she said.

I limped in after him, no tears, only hurting.

Mum and Auntie Vera broke off from preparing vegetables to give us a Christmas hug. Large pots steamed on the gas cooker, the blackened iron range in the corner already alight, cauldrons of water steaming, puddings wrapped in knotted linen cloth standing next to them, ready for the pot. The smell of two large capon chickens roasting, one in the range and the other in the cooker, flared my nostrils; my taste buds made me swallow and my rumbling tummy reminded me I was hungry.

'What time's dinner Nan?'

'You haven't had your breakfast yet.'

'Into the other room now, boys,' said Mum, lifting a large aluminium pot filled with boiling water off the range. 'The tin bath's by the fire, go and take your 'jamas off.'

'Are the girls up yet?' asked Aunt Vera.

At that moment we could hear small footsteps pattering down the bare wooden staircase. The two girls entered the room shivering. 'Mum, Nan, we got a doll each,' they said dragging the dolls by their plaits, their arms flailing from side to side.

'Don't talk with your mouths full. Take those sweets out immediately – you'll spoil your breakfast.' Mum held her hand out. The girls spat their sweets into her upturned palm.

'You two, nighties off and into the bath quickly.' Nan clapped her hands.

Mum poured the steaming water into the tub, while Aunt Vera added cold water from another enamel pot. Mum dipped her elbow into the swirling water, nodding at the same time to Vera. 'It's ready. Right, boys and girls, in you get.'

We all scrambled in, naked as the day we were born. The waist high water felt good, the warmth soaking into our bodies. The girls giggled with delight. Mum and Vera knelt down beside us and began to lather us all up with red blocks of Lifebuoy soap. The fire crackled in the grate with four towels warming next to it.

'Mum, I've got soap in my eyes,' cried June. 'Quick, Mum, it's hurting.'

Mum grabbed a flannel, held June back by her hair and rinsed her eyes. 'Now don't make a fuss, girlie,' she soothed, and June stopped struggling.

When she had rinsed us all off with the white enamel mug, Aunt Vera got out the nit comb, its very fine teeth so close together nothing could escape its jaws. She ran it through our hair. 'They're all clean,' she declared.

'Out you get now,' said Mum.

We all stood up together, our bums to the fire. We were lifted one by one from the tub and wrapped in warm soft towels. Mum, Aunt Vera and Nan rubbed us vigorously.

'Get dressed quickly,' cried Nan, 'otherwise you'll catch your death of cold.' Four sets of freshly ironed clothes hung on the wooden clothes horse. 'First one dressed gets an extra spoon of treacle on their porridge.'

The girls never rushed but Bob and I set about dressing with a vengeance; competition in everything we did bubbled through our veins. Vest first, then Y-front pants. You could never find the opening in them when you needed it, but then your todger would keep falling out at the most inconvenient times. After the Y-fronts came the shirt, buttoned up all wrong. Socks next. Why did they always end up at the bottom of your shoes – most uncomfortable – or one stayed up while one fell down. Anyway, trousers next, short ones, just above the knees: first one foot off the ground – a fine balancing act – and then the next foot up and into the trouser leg. In his haste to beat me, Bob's left foot was half wedged in the trouser hole and half caught firmly in the lining. Losing his balance, he began to hop around the room like a demented chicken, frantically trying to regain his balance.

As he lost the battle, Nan screamed at him. 'Bob! Bob!' He let go of his trousers and tried to save himself. Instead, he made a beautiful belly flop straight back into the bath. Mum, Nan and Vera screamed. Grumps came running downstairs, rubbing his eyes, just as the bow wave left the bath and extinguished the fire with a great whoosh of sparks noise and steam.

'What's all the racket about then? Some of us were trying to sleep.'

As Bob emerged wide-eyed above the rim of the bath, Grumps caught him and walloped him behind his left ear. I watched his ear turn bright red before my eyes.

'You stupid boy!' said Grumps, pulling him by his dripping hair from the tub. He shook him like a rabid dog.

'Now, Albert,' said Nan, 'go easy on the boy. After all, it's Christmas Day.'

'We-ell,' said Grumps and duly dropped him back into the bath.

'Albert!' said Nan threateningly.

'We-ell,' said Grumps and walked out of the room.

'Albert, you come back here this instant, we need you to take the bath into the back yard.'

Grumps re-entered the room, muttering under his breath, grabbed the bath by the handle, dragged it through the scullery and opened the kitchen door. 'It's bloody cold out here,' he complained, standing there in bare feet and pyjamas. Nevertheless, he easily upended the tub. What was left of the soapy water steamed its way down the path and into the garden, soaking into the mud. The chickens ran forward, pecking at the edges of the murky steaming scum as if they knew from times before that worms would emerge, irritated by the soapy mess.

Bob stood dejectedly by the dead fire, dripping water over the hearth and onto the fireside rug.

'Take them clothes off immediately,' cried Nan. 'You'll catch your death of cold. You'll have to wear yesterday's clothes until these are dry.'

Bob struggled to get his wet clothes off. The two girls stood in pink dresses with puffed sleeves, their hair tied back with matching ribbons; cream shoes and white socks finished off the angels.

'Now you two, when you've eaten your breakfast go and play with your new toys outside, but don't make much noise; your dads are still asleep upstairs. Now go.'

'Yes, Nan,' they piped as one, and left.

Why are girls so goody goody when they are young and then change when they get older? I thought to myself. From the look on Nan's face, I could tell she was thinking the same.

As we ran out, the sound of 'Don't forget to put your gloves and scarves on,' chased us down the hallway.

'No, Nan.'

Out in the cold, steam streamed from our mouths and the frost and snow made our ears glow red. I looked down our road, which was covered in whiteness: icicles hung from snow covered boughs; smoke from chimneys was trapped between branches; the cavities in the broken homes on the bomb site were filled in with deep penetrating snow, and steam from our laughter drifted upwards. This was our magical white Christmas. My heart pounded with excitement. In the dim early morning, light flowed out of nearly every house onto the snow-covered pavement, as other kids – miniature people similarly attired in beige duffle coats, gloves, scarves and hats – began to emerge from their dwellings.

'What yer get, Bob, Eric?' Billy Smith's open steaming mouth shouted at us. We ran towards him laughing, brandishing our new guns in front of us. Bob's was already primed with deadly spud. He fired it at Billy as we ran towards him. The piece of spud plopped at his feet. 'Missed!'

We glanced into other houses as we ran, all reminding us of our own: roaring fires pushed back the cold; paper chains hung from every ceiling; mums and dads walked around with silly paper hats on; new Christmas scarves were flung carelessly over some dads' shoulders, and mums sported new cardigans. Many waved to us through the windows, with a Christmas smile. Many a haggard mum's face was merry with enjoyment during the family festive season – only two days long, but magical.

Bob slid the last few feet on the snow. 'That's a good idea: let's make a slide.' We started impacting the snow with our leather shoes.

'Betcha I can slide longer than you,' challenged Billy.

'No you can't. Betcha six shots of me spud gun,' said Bob. 'What you gonna bet?'

Billy thought for a moment with pursed lips. 'Six sucks of my new gobstopper.'

'Righto. Who's going first?'

'Let's do paper, scissors, stone … three goes each … right hand behind your back. One, two three, go!' Bob pulled out his hand, shaped like a rock. At the same time, Billy pulled his outstretched hand in the shape of paper.

'I win! Paper wraps stone.'

The next go was a draw, they both pulled paper.

'No cheating!' Bob hated to lose at anything. 'One, two, three, pull!' Bob pulled scissors, Billy stone, blunting the scissors.

'I won!' shouted Billy.

'You cheated!' cried Bob, going red. 'You pulled your hand out a split second after me, you cheat.'

Billy lunged for Bob and slipped on the impacted snow, banging his nose hard on the frozen road, giving himself a nosebleed. I laughed.

'It's not fair,' cried Billy, holding his dripping nose. 'I'm going to tell my mum on you.' He retreated towards his house.

'Serves him right,' said Bob.

'You're a bad loser, Bob,' I said.

'Don't you start! Let's finish the slide.'

We scuffed our feet backwards and forwards until the frosty snow shone for about ten feet. Other kids joined in.

'Form a line. Me first,' said Bob. He ran as fast as his feet would go, jumped on the slide, one foot in front of the other, slithering along the whole length. When he reached the far end, he stopped abruptly, fell

39

over and rolled in the snow. He got up laughing. One after the other, we all had a go. The slide slowly got longer and longer. More kids joined in until everyone got bored.

The first snowball got me right on my frozen ear, stinging like crazy. As I turned, the next one caught me in the eye. Right! War! Snowballs magically appeared, pinging every which way. Coats got covered, woollen gloves became soggy. I got Bob right down the back of the neck. He got me in my other ear. I think I was deaf for a week, and with a reddened eye.

'Boys!' boomed Nan. 'Dinner's ready!'

Suddenly our tummies took priority. Other parents called their offspring for the family Christmas dinner – the once a year get together except for funerals. Doors slammed and we gave the road back to the birds, badgers and foxes. Christmas peace descended on road after road. Muffled laughter from many houses echoed down the empty street.

Scratches

Whenever we were fed up with the grown ups, Bob and I would run up to our sanctuary – our bedroom – and Christmas night was no exception. The fire glowed warmly in the grate. All was well in our little haven, especially after the best Christmas pud ever and home made crackers with little metal toys inside. The jokes were awful. For example: *Why is an elephant musical? Because it keeps blowing its own trumpet.* We laughed anyway.

Our new toys were piled in pride of place next to the fireplace, ready for another day. Also next to the hearth lay two sets of plimsolls or 'bumpers' as we called them, our universal footwear and sports equipment for football, cricket, running and jumping.

There too, casually scattered across the floor, lay familiar things from my frequent overnight stays at Nan's in the past. There were the homemade sword and shield, the sword made from a broom handle, with a piece of gold coloured cardboard stuck on as a guard and elastic bands wound around the handle for a grip. The end of the 'blade' was painted red, depicting blood. The round shield was made from plywood, with a dozen shoe studs hammered round the edge. A rough dragon with studded yellow painted eyes stared at us and a fiery red tongue licked out. There were two loops at the back of the shield, one to put your arm through, and one that you

41

gripped with your hand. These were made from one of Dad's or Grumps' old leather belts.

A scuffed, stitched brown leather football half poked out from under the bed. The stitching holding it all together had often cut my forehead when I'd been stupid enough to head it. A few copies of the *Beano* and *Dandy* were piled on the bed along with Bob's favourite, the *Eagle*. Not for me though, I preferred Desperate Dan and Lord Snooty. June and Chris's rag dolls peeked out from under the bedclothes. Nighties hung from a wire hanger on a picture frame. A few more girlie things were piled into a cardboard box – they never held any interest for us, too sissy.

Above us, stained candy-twist wires hung down from the ceiling, leading down to a brown bakelite holder with a flyblown light bulb and a pull switch attached to one side. Hanging from this was a balsa wood glider with a twelve inch wing span; R.A.F. logos embellished the wings and the fuselage.

At the window, an old pair of curtains hung to the floor. To my knowledge they'd been there since 1900-and-frozen-to-death. The distempered walls and ceilings were blue-grey with age, looking dully down on the bed below. There were cobwebs in high corners, and dusty picture rails holding up blackened chains attached to dark mahogany frames. Brown spotted pictures of aunts and uncles long forgotten stared out into the room. Granddads with high starched collars and Oxford bags gazed into their future, our past. Smiling children stood in front of a magnolia tree, its petals drifting to the ground, depicting some long forgotten spring time. There were boys in sailor suits, and girls in frilly cream frocks and bonnets tied with flowing ribbons. Great mounds of curly hair was piled under a hat held up with tiny laced hands while cherub lips puckered, pouting with indignation at the very thought that someone could take a picture of her while she was in this mess. Dewy feet shuffled in damp grass. All this, left from one instant in time.

To me, my ancestors' souls were locked in these fading, sepia pictures. What were they like? Who were they? What were their loves and hurts? What did they think, say and do? Who were their lovers, husbands and wives? Where did the laughter and tears go? Who were their friends? A little Pekinese dog, frozen in time, wagged its tail, looking up dutifully and lovingly. A little bell was tied around its neck, possibly tinkling away. What was its name? Fifi? Lulu? Charlie? Who knows? Great Grandmama stared dolefully down at me in her ruched collar and spreading crinoline dress, its puffed sleeves almost brushing her cheek. Her throat was adorned with a cameo brooch on a piece of ribbon. And how did she get that long pin to go through her head to hold on that fluffy, bulbous hat at such a jaunty angle?

To me they spoke out with honest eyes. 'Live your life. Don't waste it. You only have *now*. No yesterday or tomorrow: only *now*.'

The brass bed dominated the room. Starlight twinkled off the copper-coloured uprights. The bed springs see-sawed to the imagined sound of lovers' embraces.

'Right, Bob,' I whispered, 'you ready?'

A muffled sound came from across the room as the girls huddled by the fire, almost asleep. I stood poised over the dimly lit mattress, a block of soft Lifebuoy soap in my hand. Bob groped for the bulbous porcelain and brass light switch. 'Turn it on, Bob.' The room flooded with light from the single ceiling bulb. I blinked for an instant. They scattered in all directions. Rapidly, I patted the bed with the soap, chasing them this way and that, catching them before they could get to the seams of the mattress. 'Come here you little bleeders.'

Bob laughed at my unintentional pun. 'That's funny, Eric. How many you got?'

I turned the gooey soap over. 'About a dozen.' Some of them were still squirming. 'We'll have to do it again.'

'Can't we leave it till tomorrow? I'm tired.'

'No, I hate the little perishers. They seem to bite me more than you.'

He laughed again. 'Your turn.'

We swapped places. I turned out the light.

Nan called up the stairs. 'You and the girls asleep yet?'

"Night, Nan. God bless. Thank you for a lovely Christmas'

'Me too, Mum,' said Bob.

"Night boys. Don't let the bed bugs bite.'

All signs of the bugs were now mashed in Lifebuoy. The bed remade and us snuggled in warmth, I looked at the pictures once more. Had some of those people lain in this very bed? Had the little boys and girls snuggled up warmly like us?

'Switch the light off, Bob. It's on your side.'

'But I'm warm. If I get out my feet'll get cold.'

'You're nearest. I'll do it tomorrow.'

He moved reluctantly. Just before the light went out, I could have sworn the little girl in the picture smiled down at me.

Boxing Day Races

On Boxing Day our neighbours were coming and going all day. Gifts of food and beer piled up on the kitchen and back room tables ready for the evening. Everyone was excited in anticipation of the coming entertainment. Nan, Mum and Aunt Vera hustled and bustled trying to bring some sort of order to the chaos going on around them.

'You kids, put your coats on and go out to play.'

'Not the boys, we need them,' said Grumps. 'Go and get the cats ready. A penny a bag, and make sure you don't lose any; we need 'em all.'

'Righto Grumps, leave it to us.' We set off at full pelt, eager to be helpful.

'Don't run through the kitchen!' screamed Nan. This stopped us in our tracks. 'There's boiling water in there,' she explained. 'Be careful.'

'Yes Nan.' We gingerly walked through the kitchen and out into the garden. The smells coming from all the bubbling pots and all the food on the tables made my tummy rumble. 'Can we have a sugar sandwich, please Nan?' I pleaded for the two of us.

'When you've got the cats bagged, come back in and we'll see what we've got. Those that ask don't get.'

'Look Bob, the snow's all gone.'

'Didn't last long,' he replied. Edges of snow still lurked in darkened corners. The rest had seeped into the ground, turning some parts into mud with tufts of grass poking through.

Bagging the cats was just as tricky as catching the buggers in the first place. Bob and I never argued in these circumstances: we worked as a team. Donning our gloves we approached the cat cages. The little blighters knew we were coming, I'd swear they did. Backs arched, claws unsheathed, they screamed loudly and spat at us.

'Right,' I said, 'you take the broom and push them into the corner. I'll put my hand in and grab one.'

'Be careful Eric,' said Bob.

'I know,' I said, opening the door just wide enough to get my gloved arm in, Bob standing behind me pushing the broom at the same time.

'Get back you evil bastards!' He pushed violently with the bristle end, trying to squash the cats into the corner of the cage. I lunged forward and grabbed one with my leather clad hand. The perisher wriggled and scratched, spitting at me, a ball of teeth and claws, the strength in the thing frightening. With one movement I pulled the cat out of the cage through the small opening and back into the hessian sack. I quickly closed the top before the little bugger escaped. Surprisingly, when the bag was closed the cat stopped struggling and settled down into its dark confinement. Only three more for this sack.

After five cages and half the cats bagged, Bob and I stopped for a rest, squatting on the rock hard earth, steam streaming from our noses and mouths.

'You look like you're smoking, just like our dads,' Bob observed.

I laughed and looked around the yard. Spotting some straw which had spilled out of the rabbits' cages, I went and fetched one for each of us.

46

Placing it between our fingers we held it up to our mouths and puffed the cold steam from between our lips towards the sky.

'Don't 'arf look real,' I said and we both laughed.

'Ugh, wait a minute.' Bob spat onto the ground, holding out his tongue and rubbing it with his cuff. 'Rabbits' piss!' he said, still rubbing vigorously with his sleeve. 'Tastes horrible!'

I split my sides laughing.

'Not funny. Tastes horrible,' he repeated, still spitting. 'Ugh!'

'You boys finished yet?' shouted Grumps from the kitchen door.

'Halfway,' we shouted back.

'Well come in now and have your sandwiches.' We both ran in eagerly. 'Take your muddy shoes off, wash your hands and go into the back room.'

'Righto Grumps.' We could feel the warmth on our faces from the fire crackling away in the grate. Our treat awaited us. Margarine and sugar thickly coated on the doorstop sandwiches.

'Tuck in,' said Aunt Vera.

We could just about open our mouths wide enough to accommodate the thick sandwich. Biting through the bread, I felt the crunch of the sugar, the sweetness reaching my taste buds. Lovely.

'Any cats escape?' asked Dad.

'No. I think we've had some of the little buggers before. They knew we were coming.'

Mum smacked me on the ear hard. 'Don't swear – I've told you before.'

My ears were just thawing out from the cold outside air so it hurt twice as much. Bob sniggered, spitting some food onto the table. Nan hit him from behind, right on his glowing red ear. Thwack! His eyes nearly popped out of his head. I put my head down smiling. 'Table manners, Bob, table manners.' When I looked up he was glaring at me. That look! Here we go again, I thought.

'Come on boys, get your skates on. You've got the other cats to bag yet.'

We went out into the cold once more, reluctantly leaving the warmth behind, and resumed the task of bagging the cats, only this time Bob had the gloves and I had the broom.

Once all the cats were bagged and stacked on top of each other next to the outside privy, our next task was stringing up an extension lead with bare light bulbs from the upstairs back window to the end of the garden, making sure no bulb got broken. Two strands of bare wire – one black, one red – went into the socket, held in place with two matchsticks. We plugged in and hey presto! – All the bulbs lit up. I ran back down the stairs sideways, not quite avoiding bumping into precariously stacked beer crates – bottles clinking – and hoping none would topple on me, thereby incurring Grumps' wrath. Suddenly he appeared at the bottom of the stairs, hands on hips.

'Now slow down, boy! We don't want no broken bottles or crates cracking you on the head.'

'Sorry Grumps.' I steadied myself, holding onto the stair rail. He ruffled my hair affectionately as I scooted past him into the back room. Grabbing another sugar sandwich, I disappeared into the kitchen and out once more into the garden, stuffing myself as I went.

'You get me one of those?' enquired Bob.

I shook my head, my mouth stuffed full of bread and sugar. 'Go get your own one,' I muttered.

Bob disappeared through the kitchen door. Glancing at the bags stacked up against the wall, I noticed slight movement, but no struggling. Good. The cats had settled down and were probably sleeping.

Grumps poked his head out of the kitchen. 'Can you give us a hand with the piano, Eric?'

His head disappeared back inside. I followed. My dad and Bob were already waiting in the parlour by the upright piano. The musty smell and cold unused atmosphere reached me through the warmth coming from the rest of the house. Even though the parlour had been used the day before, the dead room brought the hackles up on the back of my neck. I never liked this room.

'Right,' said Grumps rubbing his hands together, 'let's lift it onto the wheels.'

We all got hold of one end of the piano and heaved.

'It must weigh a ton,' said Dad.

'Put your backs into it,' growled Grumps.

The inanimate piano left the ground, with us grunting and groaning. Grumps slid the first set of steel wheels under and we lowered it back down. We were all breathing heavily.

'Take a break and get your breath back,' gasped Dad, leaning on the piano. After a while, our breathing back to normal, we tackled the other end, repeating our efforts.

'Now tonight all we have to do is wheel the bloody thing into the garden; there should be more men to help.'

We nodded in agreement. As we re-entered the back room there were more sugar sandwiches on offer, dripping slices as well. June and Christine were already munching and crunching on theirs.

'When you've finished those, I want you to go up and have an afternoon nap,' ordered Nan. 'No arguments. You'll all be up late tonight helping with the drinks and sandwiches. I don't want you falling asleep when you're needed the most. Now be off with you! Shoo! Scoot!' Nan clapped her hands and we shot up the stairs, still munching. June and Chris followed.

The fire blazed in the bedroom hearth and we all huddled round warming our hands.

'I'm too excited to sleep at the moment,' I said.

'Me too,' echoed Bob.

The girls began to look sleepy, their heads nodding.

'Why don't you get into bed?'

Fully clothed they both slipped off their slippers and scrambled up and under the bedclothes. Settling down, thumbs and rag in their mouths, they soon fell asleep. Bob and I sat each side of the fireplace.

'Should be good tonight: lots of pop and grub.'

'Look at this.' Bob held out his right hand. Four vivid red scratch marks ran from his fingertips to his wrist. 'Bloody tom did that.'

I showed him my knee. 'Ginger one got me before I could put it in the bag.'

We smiled at each other, the excitement too much. The fire's heat began to make us drowsy. Our eyelids grew heavy. Bob yawned. 'I'm for a kip.' We both rose and crawled into bed each side of the girls and fell instantly asleep.

A loud knock on the front door startled me awake. The closed curtains shrouded the bedroom in darkness apart from the flickering fire. I looked over at the girls who were still fast asleep, Bob too. Muffled voices were talking in the hallway.

'Come in, come in.' The words filtered into the bedroom from below. I rolled out of bed, ran my fingers through my hair, rubbing my face at the same time, and tiptoed over to the glowing fire. Sitting down, I slipped my feet into my shoes and tied my shoelaces. Muffled laughter rose from below. I crept out of the bedroom and down the stairs.

Uncle Stan, his wife and two sons stood in the back room. A ruddy faced giant with carrot hair, Uncle Stan greeted me with a nod of his head. He had no neck: his head rose out of great broad shoulders and he stood over six feet; his wife was the opposite – as wide as he was tall. Her dark furrowed brow and piggy eyes stared at me coldly. Of the boys, one was like their mother, short and stocky, the other like their father, tall and brutish. Roger, the short one, was always loud and a bully, trying to make up for his lack of height with his fist. I didn't like him and he knew it. We stared warily at each other. Tom, the older boy, came over to me, smiling.

'Hello mate, merry Christmas.'

'You too,' I replied.

The younger one stayed silent. They lived many miles from us so we didn't see them that often, mainly meeting at birthdays and Christmas.

'You boys go and play in the yard.'

We moped outside together. Roger, the squat one, walked up to the neatly stacked bags and kicked out. The cats screeched in their darkness.

'Don't do that,' I said, clenching my fists.

'You going to stop me?'

I made to move forward but the kitchen door swung open and Uncle Stan crashed through. Walking past me, he grabbed Roger by his red hair, lifted him up, shook him like a dog and brought his big open hand down across Roger's back legs, leaving large red welts from his fingers on Roger's flesh. 'I saw you kick those cats. Now go back inside.' He whacked him once more and threw him towards the kitchen door. Roger landed on his knees, grazing both quite badly. He couldn't hold back any longer: his wails could be heard halfway down the street. Holding his bum in one hand and rubbing his head with the other, he disappeared into the house.

'Bloody kids,' muttered his dad and disappeared after him.

'Phew, I'm glad that wasn't me,' I said to Tom.

'He deserved it,' he replied.

Looking up, I saw three heads staring down from the bedroom window, their eyes bulging. They had obviously witnessed the angry scene. Tom waved to them and gestured for them to come down. All three disappeared at the same time, soon to reappear in the kitchen door. They greeted Tom, Roger's mishap soon forgotten.

The light began to fade and we were called in.

'Right,' said Dad, 'all hands to the pumps. Let's get the piano out into the garden; there are enough of us now. Come on, you boys.'

We all went into the parlour. Pushing and pulling, we manhandled the piano, edging it through the kitchen and out into the garden.

'Hope it doesn't rain,' Grumps remarked. Everyone looked at the heavens.

'Doesn't look like it,' Stan observed.

'Better put a cover over it anyway,' said Dad. 'There's a couple of hours to go.'

Indoors, the women, with the girls helping, were hard at it making sandwiches. Roger sat in a chair sulking. Everyone ignored him. Some of the sandwiches next to the fire began to curl at the edges, but nobody seemed to notice. Beer glasses shone in the firelight, end to end on the makeshift trestle tables shoved up against the wall under the steamed up window. Grumps' Christmas firkin was still half full, bottles of milk stout, brown ale, Guinness, Strongbow and Woodpecker cider, as well as home-made ginger beer and lemonade, all stood to attention.

Knocks at the front door heralded the arrival of more guests. June and Christine were detailed coat duty: off with the coats, up the stairs to the third bedroom, plonk the coats down and then back downstairs again to wait for the next arrivals. Our dads were on the drinks, handing out beer to the men, sherries or milk stout to the women. Our mums were in charge of sandwiches and cakes. The parlour and kitchen soon filled up with people laughing and munching, slurping and burping their way through the grub and drinks.

'Right,' said Grumps above the noise, raising one hand to get everyone's attention. 'Thank you all for coming. I think everyone's here now.' About fifty people were shoe horned, shoulder to shoulder, into the back room. 'Thanks for all the grub and drink you've donated for tonight's games. In about half an hour, when you're all puffed and stuffed, we'll go into the garden and let the games begin.' A loud cheer bounced off the wall and almost deafened me.

With the sandwiches and cakes annihilated, the drinks began to flow freely, the noise got louder and the room filled with smoke from roll-ups, pipes, and my favourite smell – Grumps' Christmas cigar.

'Get your coats and into the garden,' shouted Grumps.

All the family women were now on coat duty. They ran up and down the stairs, handing coats, gloves and scarves back to their owners. Men, women and children began to make their way outside, refilling their glasses and beer mugs as they went. Everyone lined each side of the thick chalk lines drawn out along the whole length of the garden, about one hundred feet in all. A chalk board had been set up on the back wall.

'Who's going to be the judge at the bottom of the racetrack, then?' asked Grumps, clearly in charge of the situation. 'We need two impartial volunteers, please.' Two men stepped out from the line. 'Good on you,' said Grumps. Quietly he said to them, 'You both get a large whisky from my secret bottle.' They both grinned, grabbed their booty and headed for the bottom of the track, red flags in hand. The garden was illuminated from top to bottom, the naked light bulbs swinging in the slight wintry breeze. The night was very clear, no clouds, the moon grinning down. The cats lay quietly in their hessian tombs.

'Four volunteers for the off!' shouted Grumps. The throng of people got even louder as the drinks flowed and four bleary-eyed men wobbled forward, their beery breath steaming in the cold. 'Gloves on!' commanded Grumps. 'Bob and Eric, the first sack if you please, lively now.'

We gingerly lifted one sack, each of us holding the corners. The cats stirred in their dark confinement as we placed it carefully at Grumps' feet. The four men surrounded the sack, pulling on their thick leather gloves.

'When I open the sack,' said Grumps, 'you four grab one each. If any escape you'll have me to answer to, see.' He untied the sack, opened the top warily and shone a large torch at the cats. Four sets of startled eyes glared back at him. The bright light made them push back into the bag, trying to escape through the bottom of the hessian sack. The four men had time to thrust a hand in and grab the poor creatures by the scruff of their necks. As they hauled the cats out with one hand, they grabbed the base of their tails with the other. Now holding the screeching, snarling, spitting animals out in front of them, they stepped up to the starting line.

'Rose, start playing,' ordered Grumps.

Nan's fingers pressed down on the ivory keys. As she hammered the piano, the audience began to sing, some in tune, some not. Nobody cared; it always sounded better when you were drunk.

> *Blaze away, blaze away, Queen of all the virgins.*
> *Tra -la-la, tra-la-la, queen of all the virgins.*
> *Oh what a pity she's got one titty to feed*
> > *the baby on.*
> *Tra -la-la, tra-la-la, queen of all the virgins.*

'Faster, Rose, faster!' shouted Grumps. 'The tote's sixpence a go. Pick your animal carefully and place your bets ladies and gentlemen.'

Everyone shouted together. 'Sixpence on the ginger one!' 'A tanner on the black!'

'All right, all right, I'll get to everybody,' he shouted as he chalked the prices up on the blackboard.

'All bets taken?' shouted my dad.

'That's the last bet for this race,' concluded Grumps, shutting his tout's bag.

'The chickens won't lay for the next few days,' Mum said to Aunt Vera. Aunt Vera merely raised her eyebrows.

'Ready with the cats? Push hard, boys.'

The cats were now flattened on the frozen earth, still spitting and screaming. The men began to pump the cats up and down, first at the front ends and then at their backs, into a rhythmic see-saw motion.

'Faster now!' commanded Grumps. 'Faster!'

The four men began to sweat, the music keeping pace with their actions.

'*Tra-la-la, tra-la-la, queen of all the virgins.*'

'When I say the word 'GO', you will release the cats. Is that clear?'

All four men nodded, all the while pumping up and down faster and faster. The cats began to wail loudly, right above the din of the shouting and singing.

'Are you ready at the bottom of the garden?' Grumps shouted to the two judges. They waved back, crouching down so as not to miss the winner. Everyone down the garden shuffled to the edge of the racing lines; some at the far end stepped forward for a better view.

'Stand back, stand back,' Grumps gesticulated, waving them away.

The men were still pumping the cats. ''Urry up, won't yer, me bleedin' arm's falling off,' complained one of them.

'All right, all right,' moaned Grumps. 'Ready, steady, GO!'

The four men released the cats, who needed no encouragement and took off with blinding speed. Straight as an arrow they sped down the garden. Cats always run in a straight line, looking for a means of escape, which in this case happened to be the dwarf wall at the bottom of the garden. Over the finishing line, they leapt the wall in full stride and were gone.

The music stopped. Nan sat there rubbing her aching wrists.

'The ginger tom won,' shouted the two judges, in agreement.

'Righto,' acknowledged Grumps. 'Who had money on the ginger tom? Show me your tickets please. Five minutes and we'll have another race.'

Mum, Aunt Vera, Dad and Jack walked along the lines of people offering them jugs of beer and cider, filling glasses until they overflowed. We all knew that the more we filled them up with drink, the more they would spend on the tote. Grumps was set to make a pretty penny out of this night; he'd make sure of that. Another bag of cats was dragged forward, ready for the next race. The tote was up and running again. Some of the winners from the last race put bigger bets on. Four more volunteers held the next lot of squirming cats by the scruff of their necks and the base of their tails so that the punters could eye them expertly. Nan rubbed her wrists, waiting for the next race. The women formed queues outside the outdoor privy; the men peed over next door's garden. And so the evening wore on.

With the assembled throng still screaming raucously, Grumps jumped up on one of the beer crates, taking a ringmaster's stance. Cupping his hands around his mouth he bellowed at the drunken crowd. 'Oi, quiet you lot! SHUT UP! I want to say something.' He waved his arms around, catching their attention. The din subsided into a drunken mumble. 'Before the evening finishes – and I can see some of you need to go home before you fall down ...' He paused for effect, smiling at the slurred laughter which greeted his remark, 'we have some booze over, so I think this calls for a competition.' The laughter from the crowd turned into cheers. 'Now, four bottles of brown ale, two bottles of stout and a jug of my finest Burton for whichever man jack of you has got the dirtiest feet.'

Several men stepped forward, grinning drunkenly, unlacing their boots and peeling off their socks. One sock disintegrated as it came off. Mr Arthur from Number 27, hopping on one foot, fell sideways laughing, still trying to untie his boot. There he lay, a boot in one hand, a gungy sock in the other.

"Urry up, Albert, me foot 'asn't seen the light of day this winter. It's fallin' off with the cold.'

'All right, all right,' said Grumps, walking along the line of swaying men. Standing in front of Henry Light, Grumps put his hand on his shoulder. At the same time he wrinkled his nose. 'Henry Light, how long since you washed your twinklies?'

'Well, let's see now,' said Henry, taking his cap off and scratching his greasy hair. 'Put these 'ollyocks on about the end of August, ready for the winter. Don't recall taking 'em off since.'

Grumps glanced down at the exposed foot, all black and green, toe jam sealing the toes together. 'I can smell 'em from 'ere. Blimey!'

'Nuffink wrong with these,' said Henry defensively. 'The missus never complains anyway.'

'Well you're the winner tonight, Henry Light.'

Nan stepped forward with his prize. Henry's face nearly fell in half, his yellow teeth showing from ear to ear. 'The last drinks are on me,' he shouted, pointing at his prize.

'Good ol' 'Enry,' someone shouted out. The crowd surged forward, clinking glasses in hand. Many of them slapped Henry on his back as he poured beer into their glasses and some onto the ground. I sneaked up behind Henry, glass in hand, holding my nose at the same time. Kneeling down on the damp earth, I held out the stolen glass between his legs, catching the spilling beer, froth and all. Holding the illicit beer close to my chest, I weaved between the crowd until I spotted Bob.

'Bob, look what I got.'

'Cor blimey, let's have a sip.'

'Not a sip, half each.'

We grinned conspiratorially, sliding behind the shed, taking care not to spill a drop.

'Put your boots back on and go home. The party's over,' I heard Grumps shouting from his soapbox.

Everyone began to shuffle towards the kitchen door, wishing each other goodnight.

'Wipe your muddy feet as you go through,' shouted Nan. She never gave up on the war on grime.

'What are you doing with the rest of the cats?' asked Henry.

Grumps glanced down at the remaining sacks. 'Usual,' he said casually sipping his beer.

'Put me down for one, but don't tell the missus. It'll be a treat for 'er.'

'OK,' said Grumps. 'Pop in tomorrow for it. But don't have it for three days, see. Let it 'ang. Be much better then.'

'Righto,' said Henry. He doffed his cap and left.

'Boys, where are you?' Grumps peered around the garden.

'Coming Grumps.'

We hurriedly finished our beer. Standing up, Bob accidentally burped in my ear.

'Sorry, Eric.'

'That's all right, Bob. Can't feel anything. Me ears are numb with cold anyway.'

'There you are, boys! Put the rest of the cats back into the cages. Tomorrow you can clear up the garden.'

We looked around. The place looked like the bomb site across the road. Bob scratched his head. 'This'll take hours,' he moaned.

'Never mind, we don't have to do it till tomorrow. Just as well. I'm tired.' I rubbed my eyes and yawned my way indoors. As I dragged my weary feet up the darkened staircase leading to our dreamroom, the whole evening replayed itself in my mind. An involuntary beery burp left my lips. 'Please, God, can we do it again?'

The girls were already fast asleep. I don't remember stripping off, but I was soon aware of snuggling up to June, her warmth warming me.

'Hello pillow, hello blanket,' I heard myself say. Sleep covered me with its own blanket and I remembered no more.

The next morning the sound of the great brass knocker reverberated down the hall, catching Grumps' ear out in the garden. 'They're early,' he muttered under his breath. 'I 'aven't quite finished yet.' He wiped his bloodied hands on his apron, the blood soaking into the cloth. I watched fascinated. The skinned animals hung on meat hooks, dripping their life force onto the dirt below. The blood turned to a dirty brownish red as it mixed with the soil.

'Get the door, will ya, Rose? It's probably my first customer.'

'Righto, Albert, but keep yer 'air on, me 'ands are covered in flour. I'll be a tick.'

The knocker boomed again.

'For Chrissake Rose, 'urry up! There's money banging on that door. I don't want to lose any customers.'

'All right, all right Albert! You're getting my knickers in a twist.'

'You can't tell your arse from your elbow, so don't worry about it,' he retorted through the open scullery door. I stood there open-mouthed. My Nan and Grumps were always joshing each other good-humouredly. I didn't quite understand it but their banter always fascinated me.

Henry Light stepped through the door, his cap

in his hands. 'Hope I'm not too early, Albert? I want to 'ang it up before the missus gets 'ome. Surprise like. Might get me end away tonight.' He stood there grinning, his hair flat with Brylcreem. The inside of his cap was stained a dirty yellow.

'I fink you should wash them feet before you get in too much of a lather. The smell of them could waft all the way to the 'igh street.'

Henry laughed, exposing his yellow teeth to the sunlight.

'You got your ninepence?'

The cap-twiddling idiot nodded. Still grinning, he reached inside his waistcoat and pulled out some shiny coins. Holding the money in his outstretched dirty palm, he walked towards Grumps, who took the coins from him and reached up to one of the dripping corpses. I could see his hands and forearms stained with blood.

''Ere we are then, a kidney free 'Ostend rabbit'.'

'Lovely,' said Henry. 'The missus will be pleased with that.'

Grumps wrapped it in newspaper, the blood already soaking through. 'Now don't forget to 'ang it for a couple of days – sort of tenderises the little perisher. Tell your mates I've got a few more 'anging up 'ere ready for the pot. A shilling each. You got yours cheap for 'elping out last night.'

'They won't 'ang around for long. Thanks, Albert.' He turned and disappeared through the scullery door.

'Get a sack, Eric. I want these cats 'eads and skins dumped down the sewer before tonight.'

'Yes Grumps.' I disappeared after Henry to get a sack, my taste buds salivating as I thought of the rabcat stew we would have in a couple of days. Maybe

Grumps would keep two and we could be having baked rabcat as well.

As I now look back fondly, the memories running through my mind are still vivid: the cats, the crowd – so individual –, the aching cold, my innocent cousins and sister all glowing with excitement, the peace and security surrounding us. The candour and the cruelty were a way of life, the family all important and an open door policy for all the neighbours, all but gone now.

Nine Lives

After the last rabcat left the building, Nan walked out of her kitchen. 'Right,' she said, 'I'm off for my kip.'

'You checked all your cats are out, Nan?'

''Course I 'ave, lovey. Don't want to 'urt any of the little perishers, do we?' My nan loved her cats. Funny she didn't mind eating the rabcats, though. 'Give me an hour for forty winks then wake me up with a large cuppa, Eric.'

'Yes Nan.'

I heard her thump her way upstairs. She was a big woman, but no one would say that to her face. I sat down next to the range, poking at the embers, watching spirals of hot grey ash flutter onto the hearth, making little piles of dust. The cats and dog were curled round my feet, making the most of the warmth. The smell coming from the cauldron above the fire stead was making my mouth water. All the leftover bits from our Christmas meals were stewing away: chicken bones, a few spuds, old greens, carrot scrapings, an old marrow bone. If it was food it went in. Stew was our main meal on a midweek night. My Nan kept it topped up with water and Bisto; a little bit of salt and pepper finished off a stew that was the best I've ever tasted. I sat there listening to the rhythm of the kitchen clock, aware of the mesmeric ticking of time.

'Er-iiic!'

A shrill scream pierced the air, making me jump. My daydreaming came to a halt.

'ER-IIIC!' Nan screamed again.

I ran up the stairs. 'Coming, Nan.' She was standing by the bed, one hand on her ample hips, the other pointing down, a shocked look on her face. I stood next to her, looking at the thing on the bed. The poor thing lay there spread-eagled on the bedclothes, claws drawn, tongue hanging sideways, eyes bulging out of their sockets. A flat cat.

'I *told* you to check for cats,' I reminded her.

'I did. It must've crawled in when I came down to tell you I was going for a kip.'

'What are we going to do, Nan?'

She scratched her curler-covered head thoughtfully. 'Pick the cat up and bring it downstairs. I've got an idea.'

She thundered her way down as I gingerly picked up the cat, still warm but as flat as Grumps' cap.

'Hurry up, Eric,' echoed up the stairs.

'Coming, Nan.' I ran down with the flat cat in my outstretched hands. Even its tail hanging down was flat.

'Come in 'ere,' she boomed. 'Now lay it on top of the piano. Good boy. Now go and get the salt tin from the kitchen. You know where I keep it. Hurry now.'

I ran through to the kitchen, grabbed the tin and dashed back. Her large hands scooped great handfuls of salt.

'We've got to cover the whole cat.'

'That won't be hard, Nan.'

'Now don't be cheeky.' Rivulets of tears ran down her pink jowls. 'Poor little thing. One of me favourites.'

64

I knew what she was doing. One of our parlour games was to catch flies and put them in a jar of water. When the flies stopped wriggling and we were sure they were dead, we would scoop them out, put them on a piece of paper, then cover them in salt. We'd watch as the salt began to move and the fly struggled out to fly away. It made us kids laugh.

'I don't know if this is going to work, Nan.'

'Well it does with the flies.'

'I know, Nan, but this cat ain't been in no jar.'

'I know, I know, but give it a chance.'

'Nan, you go and make yourself a nice cuppa and I'll keep dogeye.'

'You're a good boy.' Nan wiped her tears on her pinny and shuffled out of the room, still crying.

Poor Nan. Except for the grains that trickled onto the ivory piano keys, the pile of salt never stirred. I tweaked the flat cat, looking for some movement, more in hope than conviction. I heard Dad's motorbike pull up outside. The engine spluttered to a stop, and then he scraped the key into the front door and walked in

'In here Dad.'

'Hello son.' He kissed me on the top of my head. 'What's up?'

'Nan fell asleep on a cat.'

'Cor blimey, let's 'ave a look!'

'It's under the salt, on the joanna.'

Dad brushed the salt off the cat, spilling it all over the piano and the floor. 'Cor, luvaduck, it's flat! It'll make a good paddle or a bat, but it's never going to be a cat again. Go and put it in the dustbin, Eric. I'll go and see Ma, tell her it got up and ran away.'

'Mum!' Dad walked towards the kitchen. 'That bloody cat just ran out the front door.'

'Ah never mind, it'll come back when it's 'ungry.'

I said goodbye to the cat as I lowered it into its dustbin-coffin.

Lucky it Wasn't Me

Winter came and went. Spring appeared: daffodils bloomed, followed a little later by tulips. We still lived at Nan and Grumps' house. They seemed to have absorbed us into their family. Bob and I, cooped up for long winter months, had constantly argued or fought until Grumps or my dad parted us with whacks round our ears. Now that the lighter evenings and warmer days appeared, we played more amicably together.

'Did you get it, El?'

'Sure did!' I held out my right hand: two of Grumps' discarded dog ends lay in my upturned palm.

'Cor, don't they pong!' remarked Bob.

I nodded, wrinkling my nose at the pungent smell emanating from the dead fag ends. 'You got our pipes?'

Bob nodded back. He removed his hand from inside a secret hole at the back of the chicken and rabbit hutches. This place was our hideaway from the adults: a small gap between the fence and the coops, just enough for us to squeeze behind. There in his hand were two dried acorn pipe bowls, which we'd stashed away in autumn after removing all the pulp and scraping them clean with our secretly-hidden-away, slightly broken, rusty army knife. While I'd gone to pinch the dog ends from Grumps' ashtray, Bob had made a tiny hole in the side of one acorn. He inserted a clean length of hollow straw, put the pipe to his lips, sucked in imaginary smoke and blew hard.

'Lovely,' he said, winking at me.

'Can I have a go, Eric?' Bob and I were squatting behind the coops with our tobacco-filled home made pipes, all ready to spark up and here *she* was, spoiling our fun.

'You're too young, June.'

'Go on, let me have a go.'

Bob looked at me.

'I know, wait here.' I scurried out from our hiding place. Quick as a flash I disappeared back indoors. Grumps' dead ashtray still lay there. I picked up another dog end and legged it for the back yard, crouching once more in our hiding place. I handed the dog end to my sister. 'There you are, June.'

'What do I do?'

'Well, before you light it, I want you to practise. Put it between your lips and suck and blow just like our dads.'

She placed the dark-stained mashed end between her pouting lips.

'Now suck and blow, go on.'

The dead end of the brown, spittle blown dog end moved in and out, her lip movement exaggerated.

'That's it, now faster, in and out.'

A sudden gurgled cry left her mouth. 'Ugh! I've swallowed it. It tastes 'orrible.'

'Well it serves you right, you puckered too hard.'

June began to cry, rubbing her throat. 'Tastes 'orrible,' she repeated, spitting onto the ground, trying to rub the taste away with the back of her hand. 'I'm going to tell Mum.' She stood up, still crying.

'Girls just don't know how to play grown up games,' I said, as Bob and I put our pipes to our lips.

68

'Give us a light, Bob.'

We both put our pipes to the flaming match, sucking together. I saw Bob's face mirrored in mine: the burning sensation in our throats was excruciating and our faces turned bright red. We choked and coughed at the same time, clutching at our throats.

'Me throat's on fire,' Bob spluttered through the smoke. His eyes turned red and began to water.

'It tastes 'orrible.' I nearly fell over as a dizzy spell enveloped me. 'Cor, why do they do it? It must be some sort of punishment.'

Bob threw away his acorn pipe. 'Well if that's being grown up, I don't want nothing to do with it.' We coughed our way back indoors.

'You boys been smoking?'

'No Nan.'

'Yes you have, I can smell it on you.' She boxed our ears. 'Now go to your room. You wait till your fathers come home: you'll get more than a cauliflower ear, I can tell you.' She chased us through the back parlour with a saucepan in her hand. We ran up the stairs two at a time, slamming the bedroom door behind us.

'Well if that's smoking, you can keep it.' (Bob never smoked again for as long as I knew him.)

'Albert,' called Nan, 'we need a chicken for Sunday. The light tan one's stopped laying. She'll do.'

'Right,' grunted Grumps, turning towards the chicken coop. He undid the latch and went in. The chickens always seemed to know what was coming. Perhaps they had a sixth sense. The light tan one sat on her perch, waiting; all the others in the corners. At the last moment she puffed out her chest, Grumps took her by the neck – one quick twist – and

69

her life ended. A few flutters of her wings and beats of her heart and it was all over.

'One more for the pot,' mumbled Grumps. He called out for June who was standing shyly in the back doorway, head down, hands in front of her frock. 'Come over here,' he said, the chicken hanging limply from his hand. 'Grab that stool, and sit down.'

June did as she was told. I knew what was coming next. My initiation had taken place two years earlier. Grumps plonked the chicken on her lap, its head with its dead eyes swinging from side to side, its warmth reaching through to her skirt.

'Start plucking.'

She flinched.

'Now, girl, don't be silly. You've seen your mother and Nan do this many times, and you've got to learn sometime.'

She hesitated, lifting her hands off the bird. Losing his patience, Grumps leant over and started to pull the feathers out in clumps. The chicken's feet began to move up and down and the dead-eyed head rolled from side to side. June leapt up crying.

'Mummy, Mummy,' she screamed, running into the house. She grabbed Mum's apron and tried to hide. Great gulps and sobs came from within the folds of the pinnie.

'What's up, my petal?' Mum asked.

Grumps stomped into the kitchen with the partly plucked chicken. June screamed.

'Silly girl,' said Grumps. 'Only showing her how to pluck it.' He held the bird out in front of him for confirmation. June screamed again.

'Now don't be silly,' said Mum. 'It can't hurt you, can it? It's dead. Now go with your granddad and do as you're told.' She pulled June from her, shook her roughly and pushed her towards Grumps.

Again June screamed. Mum lost her temper, slapping June across the backs of her legs. The finger marks soon began to redden on her skin. She wriggled, trying to escape. Mum shook her again and began to drag her into the yard. 'Now sit down!' she said, anger rising in her voice. By now, June was crying uncontrollably with pain and horror. I bit my lip, my instincts to protect my sister strong within me. She wriggled like an eel, with Mum holding onto her wrist, her fingernails digging into her flesh. 'Sit down, girl, and stop this, or I'll hit you again.'

Mum had a short fuse and this had set her off again. I hoped she wouldn't go too far, or we'd be seeing her off on another 'holiday'. To us kids this was everyday life. I thought all families were like us.

Gentle Aunt Vera was standing in the kitchen doorway with tears in her eyes. She knew that when her sister lost her temper nothing and no one could dissuade her. 'Joyce, go easy on her. She's only young.'

'Shut up and mind your own business,' hissed Mum, shooting Vera a glance which said 'One more word and you're next.' Vera retreated into the kitchen. Mum turned her attention back to June. 'Now stop this at once, or I'll hit you. Sit down! Now!'

June sat down.

Mum plonked the still warm chicken on her lap. 'Now pluck!' she said menacingly.

June picked up a feather and pulled with trembling fingers. Great hiccupping sobs came from her chest. Mum leant down beside her and began to help, her temper dissipating slightly.

'Now don't be so silly,' she said. 'You'll sit here until every feather has been plucked.'

'That's what you get for being soft on them when they're young,' remarked Grumps.

71

'Dad, stop interfering,' Mum snapped.

'Just making a comment,' said Grumps, sidling off.

An hour later June was up to her knees in feathers, still sobbing. Grumps came back.

'Silly girl' he said, and walked away. He turned to look at me. 'I don't know what you're staring at. It's your turn now. Come here, son. It's about time you learnt to kill a rabbit.' He waved his arm, beckoning me towards him.

Mum still stood staring down at my sister, her bleach-reddened hands on her hips and her angry red face puffed out, as June's tears flowed down her cheeks and dripped onto the dead chicken on her lap.

Nan came out and lifted her up from the surrounding feathers, the smell of dead poultry all over her. 'Now girlie, let's top and tail you, ready for bed,' she said gently.

June fell asleep across her shoulder before she reached the kitchen door.

'Right lad.' Grumps had come up behind me and started pulling me away from the scene, my distress for my little sister showing on my face. 'See that stick over there?' I glanced in the direction he was pointing. 'Go and get it. We're going to need it.'

My concentration was broken and my thoughts shifted to the task in hand. Grumps walked to the rabbit cages. Selecting one, he grabbed the thing by the scruff and pulled it from the cage. The other rabbits looked on dolefully.

'Now,' said Grumps, holding out the poor creature and dangling it in front of me. Its head bobbed up and down and its paws punched the air reaching for somewhere to gain purchase. Grumps flicked his wrist, upending the rabbit, grabbing the back legs and letting go of the scruff of its neck. The

72

rabbit bucked up and down a few times before dangling with nose twitching and ears erect. It looked out with bulbous eyes at its upside down world.

'Right,' said Grumps. 'See how it's gone all quiet like?' I nodded attentively. 'You run your hand down its back, like this.' I watched as his hand quickly ruffled the fur. Its head shot out in surprise. 'See that?' observed Grumps.

Before I had time to comment, he brought his bladed hand swiftly down on the outstretched neck. There was an audible snap. The creature's eyes glazed over, a few nerves made the carcass twitch up and down, and then it went limp.

'There you are.' Grumps walked to the back wall and hung the rabbit on a hook. 'Be good to eat in three days time.'

The black furred body, its pink tongue protruding between its razor sharp teeth, dripped its life's juices onto the mud below.

'Your turn.'

A sad-eyed rabbit looked out from its confinement, a sixth sense telling the creature it was about to meet its maker. I reached in and grabbed it, just like Grumps had done.

'Right, boy, turn it upside down. That's it, that's it. Now, grab that stick firmly.'

I stroked the stick down its back.

'Good boy.'

The rabbit stuck its head out.

'Now 'it it 'ard.'

The sweat on my palm made the heavy stick slippery. I swung it down towards the rabbit as hard as I could. Before it reached my victim, the stick flew from my grasp. True as an arrow it travelled with great speed towards Grumps, hitting him right on his 'wedding tackle'. A great yelp left his cavernous mouth and he cupped the offended area with both hands.

'Gawd, luvaduck!' His face reddened and his knees buckled.

'Sorry, Grumps! Does it hurt?'

''Urt, you silly git?' He heaved great lumps of breath in and out, in and out.

'Sorry, Grumps,' I repeated.

'I'll give you sorry when I get me breath back.'

At that moment, Dad walked through the kitchen door, home from work. 'What's up Albert?' He spotted the stick lying at Grumps' feet; he saw him clutching his nuptials and a grin spread across his face.

'Don't you laugh! It's not funny,' gasped Grumps.

'Sorry, Albert, couldn't help but see the funny side. Mum won't be at all pleased.' Dad still grinned down at poor old Grumps. 'What you been doing anyway?'

'Trying to teach your boy how to kill a rabbit,' Grumps said between gasps.

'Killed your knobbly stick instead, eh, Albert?'

'I told you it's not funny. I'm going to be sore for a week.'

Dad walked up to me. I was still clinging onto the hapless rabbit.

'There is another way to kill it. Give it here.' He took the poor creature from me, tucked it under his left arm and held his right hand in front of me. 'You know Mr Churchill's V sign?'

'Yes Dad.'

'Well it's sort of the same but in reverse.' His hand, knuckles out, showed just two fingers, pointing to the sky. 'Now watch carefully.' He placed his V shaped fingers under the rabbit's throat, a finger of his other hand behind its ears, and tightened his grip. 'Can you see what I've done?'

'Yes, Dad.'

'Then you just pull.' The muscles in his forearms began to bunch, the veins on his neck swelling. The rabbit's eyes popped out of their sockets and a crack broke the silence. The rabbit's head lolled to one side.

'There you are, boy, another one for the pot. Go and hang it with the other one.' He wiped his sweating hand down the side of his trousers. 'Want a beer, Albert? That'll make you perky.'

'Righto,' mumbled Grumps, managing to straighten himself up. He smacked his lips, still unconsciously cupping himself with one hand as a sideways grin spread across his unshaven face.

'Sorry, Grumps.'

He ruffled my hair. 'You didn't mean it. Now where's that bleedin' beer. I'm spitting fevvers.'

My Nan

1939. My Dad at 18, standing between his twin brothers.

My sister, June, with me (left) and Bob (right).

Me at 10 years old.

Childhood over. 14 years old and working.

The Fruits of Innocence

There we were, sitting in the classroom, all thirty eight of us – the naughtiest boys from the surrounding district. It was nearly the end of the summer term, my first year at Joseph Barratt Secondary School for Boys almost over – the longest I'd ever been in one school. How long it would last I didn't know, but I expected to be there all the time we were living at Nan's.

'Right,' said Mr Allen, our year teacher, 'sit to attention, hands folded behind your back.' Rustling and fidgeting instantly became the order of the day. 'Settle down, settle down now, boys.' There was slight menace in his voice.

The first fart came from the back. Mr Allen looked up from the register.

'Who did that?'

'Sorry sir, beans on toast for breakfast. Can't help it.'

The rest of the class giggled.

'None of that.' Mr Allen slammed his ruler on to the top of his desk. 'If you don't want detention for the summer holidays, you'd better all be quiet.'

The second fart came from the front of the classroom. Mr Allen went purple.

'Stand up, that boy.'

Fatty Harris stood up, the fart exuding around him, getting louder as he rose from his desk.

'Cor, that stinks.' Charlie Jones, sitting next to

Fatty, waved his arms about, trying cut the offending smell into chunks so he could blow it away.

'Don't you blow that smell over here, or I'll bash yer.'

'QUIET!' The apoplectic teacher stood, hands on hips, eyes bulging. 'I'm not going to have any more disobedience and disruptiveness from you lot.'

'Yes sir,' the whole class said.

Mr Allen strode purposefully backwards and forwards in front of the class, staring menacingly. His tie under his tweed jacket seemed to be choking him: the veins on his face and neck stood out and his skin was all blotchy and patchy.

The next fart reverberated around the room, echoing off the windows and walls, bouncing around the classroom. Mr Allen stopped dead in his tracks.

'Sorry, sir,' said Patrick, my best friend. 'I think I've followed through. I daren't move. Please don't ask me to stand up; I've only got short trousers on.'

'SHUT UP, BOY!' We all sensed he was losing control by now. 'All of you, stand up! Now stand to attention!'

We all rose. The noise was deafening. We were all sitting on home made farting machines – a horse shoe shaped piece of flat thin metal, two elastic bands with a washer in the middle. Wind it up tight, place it under a book, sit on the whole contraption, raise one cheek of your derrière or stand up, and the washer whirred on the book, making a realistic sound of farting.

'Bring those farting— Bring those devices to me! You're all on detention for the next week. I'll be writing to your parents in due course.'

'Aw, sir, it was only a joke.'

'Same as that disgustingly realistic dog poo you left in my desk last week. You boys are here to learn, not to make jokes at my expense. It's nine fifteen and I haven't even taken the register yet. Are you all here?'

'Yes sir,' we chimed in unison.

'What's your first lesson, Eric?' He sat me in the front so he could keep an eye on me. I don't know why.

'PE, sir.'

'Aha, with Mr Hart! He'll sort you lot out. Now off you go,' he said with some relief. 'March out in line.'

We'd all made it through the start of the day. No one had got the cane yet.

'Into your PE kit quickly, now,' bellowed Mr Hart. 'Right, now form straight lines down the hall. Today we'll play Tarzan. All the apparatus will be used: wooden horse, parallel bars and ropes. You six boys fetch the wooden horse from the corner. You boys,' he said, pointing, 'unfurl the ropes, and the rest of you sit down.'

A slight man for a PE teacher, he stood in his track suit bottoms, his T-shirt sticking to his skinny chest, and looked around at all of us until the apparatus was put out.

'Stand up you lot, and form a line. Let's see how your somersaults have improved since our last lesson.' He went and stood next to the wooden horse ready to assist the boys as they tumbled over the vault. 'Go!' he commanded.

The first boy ran as fast as he could, jumped on the spring board, hurled himself up and with one bound landed flat on his face, saved from a certain broken nose by the cushions and foam the other side of the horse. We all laughed.

'None of that now, boys. Next.'

Next in line was Fatty Harris. He laboured down the line like a wounded warthog, tits independently moving up and down, bigger than any girls', his great fat blotchy legs pounding the parquet floor. His whole glutinous mass left the floor, feet planted firmly on the springboard, and then he defied gravity for a few seconds, giving the impression of a dying duck, landing squarely on the wooden horse. All air escaped from both ends in one go.

'Stupid boy,' said Mr Hart as he thwacked him across his arse as he lay there.

'Ow, sir, that hurt!'

'Get off or I'll hit you again.'

It was me next. I loved this apparatus. Tearing down the runway, I sailed over the vault, arms outstretched, touching the leather, over and landing on my feet. I'd done it.

'Have you got pants on?' accused the teacher.

'Yes sir.'

'You know my rules: only T shirts and shorts. Remove them this instant.'

'Please sir, can I go to the dressing room and take them off?'

'No, boy, take them off immediately.'

'But sir—'

'No buts, do as you're told.'

I removed my shorts, leaving my pants on.

'Hurry up, boy, we haven't got all day.'

I turned around trying to find some privacy. The other boys giggled.

'Please sir, I think I'd rather have the cane.'

He reached out for me and grabbed me around my chest, yanking me off the ground with one hand and pulling my pants off with the other. 'Now put your shorts back on. Then go to the dressing room and remain there for the rest of the lesson.'

If I'm not doing PE why have I got to take my pants off? I wondered as the other boys laughed.

He turned to the rest of the class. 'Any more boys got pants on?' he enquired menacingly. Three boys removed them quickly. 'Now that's settled, we'll get on with the rest of the lesson. Off you go, Bartholomew.'

'I hate you!' I said under my breath as I left the hall.

'Bad luck, Eric,' whispered Patrick.

After an interminable hour all the boys came crashing through the cloakroom door, shouting and fighting each other.

'Steady now, boys! Get dressed and assemble back in the hall. Hope that taught you a lesson, Bartholomew. Next time, don't be such a chump.'

'Yes sir,' I acknowledged. Under my breath I muttered, 'But I still hate you.' I must have said it too loud.

'What did you say, boy?'

'Nothing, sir.'

'Yes you did, I heard you. Now go and stand outside Mr Maxwell's office and wait for me there.'

I knew what that meant: my first caning of the week. Would it be on my bum or my hand? 'Anyone got an orange?' I shouted on the way through the hall.

A little lad came running up. 'I have.' He held the orange out in front of him.

'Thanks.' I tore off the peel and chucked the orange slices back at him. I began to rub the peel vigorously over my palms. This was supposed to take the sting out of the caning. I grabbed an essay book from another kid, and stuffed it down my trousers. 'Don't worry, I'll give it back as soon as I've seen the headmaster,' I reassured its owner. 'I'll see you in the playground.'

Still rubbing my hand with the orange peel, I walked towards the head's door. Outside his study I hopped from one leg to the other. The hall clock ticked loudly. One hour ticked away; it seemed for ever, especially as I knew what was to happen. I felt like running away but knew they would eventually find me. Finally Mr Hart appeared, grabbed me by the scruff of the neck and knocked vigorously on the door. A booming 'ENTER!' sounded. Mr Hart turned the brass handle, throwing me through the door, where I crashed into the desk in front of me. The head didn't flinch, just carried on writing.

I looked down on a silver haired giant, his massive shoulders covered by a grey suit, the bulk of him hidden behind the desk. I looked around the room, my heart beating fast. It was a small room with one window, the bricks painted half in cream and half in green, with a black border separating them. A row of canes, varying in size and thickness, hung on the wall to his right. He used each one according to the severity of the crime, and if the boy's misdemeanour warranted extreme measures, he would be caned the following morning in front of the whole school at assembly, thus deterring any boy from straying from the school's righteous path.

The headmaster carefully and slowly placed his fountain pen next to the book he was writing in, then looked up to stare me in the face. Our eyes locked for a moment. I stared back into his deep, dark, pitiless black eyes, then looked away quickly.

'You again, Bartholomew. What has he done this time, Mr Hart?'

'Talking back, Headmaster. Backchatting.'

He rose, sliding the chair back with his legs. 'Very insolent of you, boy.' He hovered over me like a giant crow, at least ten feet of him.

'Hands or bottom: what's it to be, boy?'

'Don't know, sir'

He walked to the wall, running his hands lovingly along the mounted canes, then turned, sniffing the air. 'Have you been eating oranges, boy?'

'Yes sir.'

'Another misdemeanour – eating in class. How many times have you been told?'

'Don't know, sir.'

'Don't know, don't know,' he mimicked, working himself into a rage. 'Bend over the desk.'

The smell of the desktop's leather assailed my nostrils, the Indian inkwell, all spattered with use, close to my right eye. Several pens lay out in a neat row right in front of me. I heard the cane leaving its clip; I felt him walk behind me; I heard a few practice swishes, the cane cutting through the air.

'What's that?' he said, tapping my bottom several times with the cane.

'What's what, sir?'

'That square thing poking out of the top of your trousers.' He deftly slid the offending essay book from beneath my trousers. 'You've gone from four strokes of the cane to six, you stupid boy.'

As quick as lightning, he hit my bum three times in succession. This really stung as I didn't have time to clench my bum or my teeth. An involuntary groan left my lips.

'Serves you right, boy.'

I stood up, and a little dribble of wee left my body and ran down my leg, dampening my rolled-down sock. The pain in my bottom was excruciating. The head stood over me, swishing the cane in front of me.

'Which hand do you write with, Bartholomew?'

'My right hand, sir.'

'Hold out your left hand, then. Don't want you to have any excuse for missing lessons, do we?' He bent his face level with mine. 'Now repeat after me: you're a stupid boy. Say it!' Some spittle from his open mouth landed on my cheek. His angry eyes stared at me. 'Say after me: you are a stupid boy.'

'Yes sir, you are a stupid boy, sir.'

His face turned red with anger. 'Hold out your left hand.' He brought the cane up from the floor, catching my fingertips and nails on the way. They burned with pain as the cane hovered way above his head. He brought it down with as much force as he could muster; it came swishing through the air, catching my hand in the centre of my palm with a dull thud. The pain shot up my arm, bringing tears to my eyes. I cuffed them away with my sleeve.

Mr Maxwell grinned. 'Two to go.' He hit the underside of my fingertips once more as he brought the cane up. He brought it down for the second time with all the force he could manage again. At the point of no return, I withdrew my hand. This caught him off balance and he stumbled forward trying to regain his equilibrium. He crashed his left knee onto the desk and howled with pain and rage. He hopped around the room, then leant against the wall, rubbing his offending knee with one hand. 'Mr Hart, grab that boy and hold out his left hand.'

The headmaster turned and limped towards me, reaching for another cane, the deadliest of them all – the one with its end split open. I took a step back as Mr Hart grabbed me from behind. I felt the pulse from his hot hand running down my outstretched arm. I could smell the odour from his armpits.

'Hold still, boy.'

Maxwell advanced towards my extended hand. *Thwack. Thwack.* His anger dissipated and my fingers throbbed with pain.

'Now go back to your class. I do not wish to see you again today, Bartholomew, or I'll have your mother and father here to hear about your bad behaviour. Now go.' He pointed to the door.

I shuffled out, my one good hand rubbing my bottom, the other, stinging, tucked under my armpit.

The bell went for dinner break. Relieved, I ran for the exit, heading for the outside toilets. There was just enough space behind them to allow me squeeze in between the wall and the school fence, and hide from the world. I crouched down, trying to rock away the pain.

'You all right Eric?' Patrick crouched down, peering into the dark space.

'Go away, leave me alone.' The pain throbbed through my body. 'Go away!'

He left silently, knowing my pain. In the end my bowels made me leave my hiding place. Nature wouldn't wait. The pain became a nagging irritation until I felt slightly normal again. All of us boys were used to pain.

We were not supposed to enter the school building in the lunch hour, but I sneaked back in and headed for our classroom, thinking of getting some privacy. As I approached the room, I heard voices coming from inside. I crept up and popped my head above the half-glazed door. There, sitting on top of one of the desks, was Stuart Partridge, our idol, a senior prefect, one of the top dogs in the school. He was holding court: several boys from my class were scattered around, some sitting on their hands, one picking his nose. That silly sod has clearly forgotten there's a bogey picking contest after school, I thought.

The one with the longest snotty would be the winner – no prizes, just an accolade for having the longest snot. As I entered the classroom all heads turned my way.

'Still smarting, Eric?' quipped Stuart as I walked further into the room.

'How did you know?'

'Not just me, the whole school.'

'You bet I am.' I sat down with the rest.

Stuart carried on where he'd left off. 'Where was I?'

'You were telling us about your last innings,' someone prompted.

'Ah, yes well ...' he rattled on.

I looked at my idol: over six feet tall, stubble protruding from his lantern jaw, fifteen going on fifty. He sat there, all confidence and smiles, only his school uniform telling the truth of his age.

'Have you ever had sex with a girl?' someone asked. The room fell silent.

'I beg your pardon?'

'Have you ever had sex with a girl?'

He hesitated, looking down at us, but then said, 'Yes, of course I have.'

'What's it like?'

'Well, it's very good.'

'Yes, but what's it like?' A pregnant pause permeated our little group.

'It feels better than when you masturbate,' he said.

'What's he mean?' piped up Peter, the smallest boy in our class.

'He means when you have a wank.'

'What's a wank?' asked another of our group.

'You know – hand to plank, Barclays bank, bashing the bishop, rubbing the one eyed purple monster.'

'Yes,' said Stuart, 'you have to do that before you make love to a girl.' He spoke with great authority.

'Why?' we all asked.

'Because if you don't, when you first come it's so powerful it could burst her stomach, see.' He stood up. 'I've got to go now. Duty calls.'

He left us all sitting there in wonderment.

'What are we supposed to do?'

'How do you do it?'

No embarrassment, just curiosity.

'I think you rub your pecker until something pops out – supposed to be good fun.'

So that's why I wake up with a stiffy every morning, I thought. Tomorrow I'll have a go and see what happens.

Life after that was never be the same again.

Revenge

I ran forward. Stan passed the ball through his opponent's legs and it came on to me. I heard a shout from Tom as he ran past me. I hesitated for a split second, my instincts holding me back. Stanley Matthews ran past me on my right flank. I passed the ball to him. He dribbled it past two opponents, shooting the ball across the goal mouth. Tom Finney mopped it up and deftly flicked it into the back of the net. I'd helped score another goal for England ... Another flower head whacked into the side wall.

'Come here you little bleeder! Get 'im, Jack!' boomed Aunty Ivy, the neighbour from hell. 'Stop 'im, 'e deserves a good thumping! Grab 'im, Jack!'

Why me? All I did was kick a few flower heads in Uncle Jack's garden. I didn't mean any harm.

'Come 'ere, you little bastard!' A great meaty hand grabbed me by my hair, yanking me off my feet.

'Ouch, that hurts,' I screamed.

'You wait till Ivy gets you; this is just a little tickle,' he said as he belted me round the ear, dragging me back by my hair.

'Hold 'im, Jack. I'll teach 'im what for.'

I jumped a million miles as she whacked me across the back of my legs with her cane carpet beater. I pumped my legs furiously, trying to get away as Jack held me with his dinner plate hands, fingers protruding like swollen Wall's pork sausages, blue-green veins pulsating to the rhythm of his heart.

89

Aunty Ivy thwacked my legs again. Tears welled up in my eyes and I bit my lip with the pain. *Don't cry*, I willed myself.

'That'll teach you! That'll teach you!' she squawked like a demented parrot, eyes bulging, face red with anger, and her enormous bosom bouncing up and down. Her apron was splashed with cooking fat; one stocking was up and one rolled down to her ankle – Nora Batty before she had been invented.

Jack was hanging on to me for dear life. The veins of his enormous red beak of a nose ran this way and that. His nostrils flared, and gobbets of snot splattered onto my head from his bristling nose hair. I kicked his shin in anger and frustration. He gave a cry of surprise.

'Whack 'im again, Ivy! The little perisher's just kicked me!'

I sensed her beginning to tire. The wielding of the cane became erratic, her breathing laboured. Her squawks turned into grunts. Finally she stopped and leaned on a fence post. 'That...'ll ... teach you,' she muttered between gasps.

The backs of my legs were on fire. My inflamed flesh looked like an angry road map.

'I'll see your mother later, tell 'er what you did,' said Jack, looking at Ivy for approval. She just nodded her head, still gasping for air. 'Now, go 'ome,' he said, pushing me off the pavement.

I ran to the bomb site, grabbed a handful of dock leaves and began to gingerly rub my welts. Tears welled up in my eyes once more. This time I gave in and cried with pain and anger. 'I'll get you for this, Aunty Ivy, you just wait and see if I don't.'

Some time later, I limped home and tentatively opened the front door.

'That you, Eric?' Mum's harsh greeting echoed

down the hall. 'Aunty Ivy's been over and told me what you did. Straight to bed, now! No supper for you. I'll speak to you in the morning.'

'Yes, Mum. Goodnight. Goodnight Grumps. Goodnight Nan,' I cried down the hall, tears running down my face. No reply came back.

Later, June managed to sneak me a piece of bread and marge. Nothing had ever tasted so good. It settled my hunger, but the stinging to the backs of my legs lasted many hours.

I woke the next day with Mum standing over me, gently patting me with calamine lotion on cotton wool. 'Serves you right. Those flowers were prize dahlias. Jack and Ivy were going to show them at the church flower show next week.' She screwed the top back on the calamine lotion bottle. 'Now pull your 'jamas up, clean your teeth and go to the toilet. Got to keep you regular. I'll put some porridge on, you must be hungry.'

Try as I might, I couldn't go. I strained with all my might, but my bum stayed firmly shut. Red faced, I pulled my trousers up and flushed the toilet.

'Did you go?' enquired Mum.

'No, Mum.'

'How long has it been now?'

'Don't know, Mum, probably a few days.'

Why couldn't I lie? It would be a lot easier. As I grew up I realised it was just my constitution. My body thought nothing of going two weeks before I needed to go. Not my mum.

'I'll deal with you after you've eaten your porridge. Eat it while it's piping hot,' she commanded.

Mum served everything steaming hot; we needed asbestos mouths to eat. But we got used to it. I scooped a spoonful of scalding porridge into my mouth and sucked in and out, cooling the molten substance enough for me to swallow. The bowl empty, my tummy full, I clunked my spoon down.

'Finished, Mum. Can I get down from the table, please?'

'Yes you can.' She grabbed me by the arm and led me to the toilet. 'Now you wait here.' She disappeared into the bathroom, reappearing with a bar of red Lifebuoy soap. 'Now take your trousers down and bend over.'

'Oh Mum, don't do it again. It stings.'

Mum brooked no argument. 'Bend over. Do as you're told.' Gouging out a large piece of soap, she pushed it up my bottom with her thumb. Tears forced their way out of my screwed up eyes.

'It hurts, Mum.'

'Don't make a fuss. It'll make you go. Got to keep you regular. Now sit on the pan and don't move.'

'It's burning, Mum.'

'Good. That means it'll do you good. Now sit tight until you've been.' She slammed the door and walked away.

With the soap burning inside me, I strained away. Something hit the water with a plop. I jumped up and looked around. All there was in the pan was a piece of soap. 'Finished, Mum.'

'You been?'

'Yes, Mum,' I lied.

'Well flush the khazi and go and wash your hands in the bathroom.'

Washing my hands with the remaining piece of Lifebuoy, I hopped from foot to foot, my poor bum puckered like a parrot's beak and still stinging like mad. Biting my lip, I cuffed the tears from my eyes and called, 'Can I go out and play?'

Nan called back, 'Only in the garden. I don't

want you getting your clean clothes dirty. I've got quite enough washing to do.'

I raced out of the front door and round to the back of the garden shed where no one could see me. Lying on the grass, I began to cry with indignation, burning entrails and throbbing legs. June found me lying there, tears soaking the grass.

'Don't cry, Eric, or you'll make *me* cry.' She stroked my head trying to ease my pain.

Anger and frustration took hold. 'I'll get 'em,' I said between clenched teeth. 'You'll see, I'll get 'em. When I grow up I'm not going to be like them. Mum, Dad, Ivy, Jack, all of them: they're only nice to us on birthdays and at Christmas.' I stood up, brushing the loose grass from my knees. 'Let's go and feed the rabbits.' I took June's hand and we walked down the garden path.

'Does it still hurt, Eric?'

'No,' I lied, forcing a smile on to my face as I looked down at my little sister. 'Don't worry, June, I'm all right.'

'Eric, go and get the pail and the small shovel. The milk cart's just gone by. Follow that horse and when it's been, bring it back here. I need some fertiliser for me toms on the allotment. Grumps will show you where they are.'

It was two days after my encounter with the Lifebuoy. Dad rubbed my hair affectionately as he sent me on this errand. I raced out of the gate and just saw the horse and cart disappearing round the corner. I tore down the road, pail in one hand, shovel in the other and scraping the shovel along all the garden railings as I went, the tinny noise following me down the street. My luck was in: the horse did its business as it trotted down the road. I wondered why it didn't need to wipe its bum. It pricked its grey horse ears and swished its tail, keeping first one eye and then the other on its master dashing from door to door. It kept pace as its owner worked one side of the street and then the other, his satchel by his side and carrying a crateful of milk bottles.

'Hello, lad,' he called to me. 'You come for Daisy's droppings?'

'Yes guv, me dad wants 'em for his tomatoes.' I wished I could go like that. No Lifebuoy poo from this horse. 'Cor, that's a lot of poo.' I thought I would nick a bit for myself and use it next time I had to go, in case Mum checked down the panhole. I could keep it in the back cistern. No one would know. No more soap for my bum.

'Take the lot.' The milkman put his hands on his hips and laughed, his big belly moving up and down, his peaked hat wobbling on his head. 'There's a whole pile of it down the yard, but this is the best stuff.' He pointed at the substantial mound steaming back at us. 'Fresh, that's what this is. Help yourself, lad.'

I scraped it off the tarmac and filled the bucket. Straining with the weight, I started heaving it back home. 'Aw, mister, that's heavy. And it don't 'alf smell!'

He laughed again. 'That'll clear your lungs. Off you go, lad. Tell your mother I'll be round for my money next Friday.'

I half carried, half dragged the steaming mass up the road. Half way up our turning I saw Aunty Ivy bashing a carpet with the offending beater out of the front parlour window. Then she disappeared back into the room, leaving the sash window open. My anger rose at the sight of her; the backs of my legs were still weeping and smarting with welt marks. Half running, mostly stumbling, I reached the pavement opposite her open window. She wasn't in sight. A mad thought entered my tiny brain. KILL! Before I knew what I was doing I crossed the road, bucket of poo in one hand, shovel in the other. Thwack. The first shovel-full hit Granny Ivy's picture full in the face, sliding down the polished glass. The second load skidded across the piano top, knocking over one of the Georgian lustres. (I knew about lustres – ornaments with prismatic glass pendants – having played football in my own front room. Dad had walked in just as the ball bounced off one of them, smashing it to bits. The word 'lustres' was embedded in my mind after Dad had berated me for days. I never played football indoors again.) The noise brought a voice from the kitchen.

'What's that, Jack?' squawked Ivy the parrot.

I panicked. Lifting the bucket, I hefted its odorous contents in a wide arc into the room. It looked lovely hanging off the curtains; it was a great improvement to the fireplace, and it redesigned the carpet. Turning, I ran straight across the street, jumped the nearest wall, and landed in a patch of stinging nettles. Trying to ignore the pain, I scrambled behind a dustbin, heart pounding, skin stinging, and waited.

First a scream echoed down the street, and then pandemonium broke loose. I heard the parrot jerk open the front door and I could imagine her looking up and down the street.

'You go look down the road, Jack. I'll go see Joyce. If it's that little bleeder, Eric, I'll kill 'im.' She hopped down the front step.

I clamped my hand over my mouth, trying desperately not to laugh, and crawled down the side alley, over the back garden fence and down another

95

alley into the next street, making my way down to the canal to wash the bucket and spade clean. I could still hear the noise from our street. I lay on the canal path and cried with laughter. Two hours later I strolled home.

'Any luck, son?'

'Sorry, Dad, no luck, but the milkman said there's plenty down the depot. I'll go and get you some tomorrow.'

'There's a good boy.'

He didn't see me smiling.

That evening when I was playing in the garden I saw Aunty Ivy come wobbling across the road. Instinct made me duck behind the hedge.

'I have my suspicions over this, Jack!' She was still screeching. 'I bet this is something to do with that little perisher, Eric! If 'e's got anything to do with this, I'll bury 'is 'ead in a bucket of 'orseshit, you see if I don't!' Eyes popping out of her sockets, blood pressure going through the roof, she flexed her fat arms, clenching and unclenching her fists. Jack just stood in their doorway, keeping his thoughts to himself.

'Charlie, you in?' Ivy banged on our front door, shouting through the letter box at the same time. 'CHARLIE!' Bang, bang.

Making sure she couldn't see me, I dashed down the side alley leading to the back door.

'All right, keep yer 'air on, I'm coming.'

'What's she bleedin' want?' growled Grumps as he took another pull of his beer.

She stood there, all blubber and rage. 'You seen my front parlour?'

'How could I? I've only just got in from work.'

I knew Dad hadn't gone to work that day, as Mum wasn't well again. He was obviously trying to

96

protect me, although at this point he didn't know why. 'What's up, Ivy?'

I peeked around the door frame.

'My front parlour's covered in horseshit – up the walls, floor, ceiling, everywhere.'

'What's that got to do with me, Ivy?'

'Where's Eric? I want to talk to him.'

'Wait a minute.' Dad held out his arm as if to ward Ivy off. 'You accusing my boy? How do you know it's him? It could have been anyone.'

'Your boy did my flowers; maybe 'e did my parlour.'

'You can't go accusing the boy without proof, Ivy. He may be a bit wild but he's not to blame for everything that happens down this road.'

'Well, we'll see. In the morning, I'll ask the milkman who collected manure from him today.' She turned and waddled away.

'ERIC!' dad shouted as he slammed the door. 'ERIC!'

My heart pounded. 'Yes Dad?'

'Come 'ere. You been messing around with Aunty Ivy's parlour?'

'No Dad.'

'You sure? You came back late yesterday, empty pail and shovel.'

'I told you, Mr Milkman said to get it down the yard.'

'I can just see that room. Was it still steaming on them walls?'

I saw a twinkle in his eye and I laughed nervously. The thought that he knew was a great relief. How did dads know everything before we did?

'So it *was* you?'

'Sorry Dad.'

'No good you 'sorrying' me. If your mother finds out you'll be in the doghouse for a week. What made you do it, boy?'

'She hurt me, Dad.'

'Yes I can still see the welt marks on the back of your legs.' He leaned on the hallway wall, rubbing his stubbly chin with his corn-hardened hands. 'You leave this to me, son.' He walked away, still deep in thought.

All that night I fretted, half-sleeping, half awake, my worried conscience digging at my brain like a dog gnawing at a bone. What if Aunty Ivy found out? What would she do? Or worse, what would my mum do? She'd only just come out of hospital again. Her moods were pretty unpredictable at the best of times. Round and round the thoughts went until it was time to get up. I felt as tired as the minute I went to bed. I heard the clink of milk bottles hitting the concrete step and I went stiff, my heart in my mouth.

'MILKY! MILKY!' shouted that parrot-squawk voice I knew so well. I tweaked the curtain. She stood in front of the milkman, hands on hips, accusing finger pointing towards our house. She looked around. I ducked behind the curtain. Peeking around once more, I saw Mr Milkman shake his head from side to side. He smiled genially down on her. Her mouth was open in disbelief. Milky walked away. I could feel the animosity exuding from her body. Her beady eyes looked at our house again. She shook her head and went indoors.

My heart started to beat normally. I couldn't believe my luck. Milky hadn't told her. My relief was palpable. Phew, that's a surprise, I thought. I wonder what happened there.

Dad came home from work later than usual

that evening. 'Sorry, Joyce, had to do some overtime. Dinner ready? Evenin' Mum, Albert.'

'It's been ready for two hours. It's in the oven.'

I sat watching Dad eat, his Adam's apple bobbing up and down as he swallowed.

'Mr Milky OK this morning, Eric?'

'Yes Dad.'

'It's wonderful what half a dozen eggs can do.' He smiled and winked. One of my heroes had done it again.

The Secret in the Shed

Summer holidays came, and playtime lasted most of the day after we'd done our daily chores. Bob and I were playing in the back garden, kicking a small tennis ball, when Dad poked his head round the kitchen door.

'Eric, Bob, bring that bucket of horse manure.'

'You boys follow us,' said Grumps.

We followed them for quite some way, ending up down Sandy Alley, going towards the River Lea and the canal in the middle of nowhere. We'd heard talk of an allotment but never knew where it was. A six foot high, gated, wire fence stood right in front of us. Grumps fitted the key in the lock and opened the iron door. He turned to my dad.

'Do you think they're ready, Charlie?'

Dad hesitated for a moment, staring down at us. 'Yes I think they are.' As if he was talking to himself, he unconsciously rubbed his chin at the same time. With his other hand he flicked his dark Romany hair away from his piercing green-grey eyes.

Bob and I looked at each other, excitement grinning across our faces. The first thing we saw was a large wooden shed which took up at least a quarter of the plot. The rest of the patch was mostly covered with runner beans reaching towards the sunlight, carrot leaves bent to the slight breeze, tomatoes, onions: everything to supplement our table grew here. So this was the place where all the food came from.

101

The only exception was a piece of ground about ten feet square – hard trodden earth with dark stains all over it.

Strange scraping noises could be heard within the shed, which had no side windows and one door, heavily bolted and padlocked. A skylight, high on the pitched roof, had iron bars across the glazed glass.

Grumps took out a set of keys and began to unlock the door. A deep-throated growl came from within the darkness. As he opened the door I could hear angry barks. 'Steady boys,' said Grumps, calmly. He entered the gloomy interior. We heard him speaking into the darkness. 'Steady boys ... There's a good girl.'

The smell of dog wafted from the shed, surrounding us with its pungency. Dogs out here? What for? We didn't know anything about this. Our dog at home, old Alfie, was our only knowledge of the canine world. As jet as night, with a tail that never stopped wagging, our Labrador seemed to smile all the time, always greeting us with unconditional love. What were these, and why were they locked up?

'Come in here boys, but come in slowly, no sudden movements. Do you understand?'

'Yes Grumps.'

My dad ushered us in. The smell of urine, dogs' mess and dog sweat hit us both like hammers. As our eyes grew accustomed to the gloom, we saw several cages, all with different dogs inside. A muscular blue-grey creature launched itself at the side of its cage, teeth bared as it leapt towards us, eyes bulging red with rage. It hit the side of the cage with its head. The sound of flesh hitting metal made me step back involuntarily.

'Don't worry boy, he can't get at you. Only got him a couple of weeks ago. Saw him on Hackney marshes, attacking another dog, his owner nowhere in sight – if he had one that is. No collar, you see. He followed me all the way home, though. Used the old trick. Never seems to fail.'

'What's that then, Dad?' Bob asked.

Grumps laughed and winked an eye. He placed his hand inside his trouser pocket and pulled out a dark, half-rounded piece of whatever. He held it up for us to see. Two caged dogs turned, sniffing the air. 'See?' said Grumps, pointing to the sniffing dogs. 'Never fails to work – a piece of horse's hoof. Place it in the palm of your hand, facing towards the dog, and it will follow you to Timbuktu.' My dad and Grumps laughed out loud. 'Now, boys, these is fighting dogs, see?'

Bob and I stood there open-mouthed. 'What breeds are these?'

'Staffs and English bull terriers,' replied Grumps. 'This is our secret and yours. No one must know, do you understand?'

We both nodded.

'You know what to do,' he said. He placed a hand on both our heads.

We said together: 'We promise not to tell another living soul, on pain of having our eyes poked out and our tongues slit in half.' We knew they were serious. They only made us swear on special occasions. I wouldn't even be able to tell Patrick, my best friend.

'Good. Charlie, get the treadmill, will you?'

Dad dragged a funny looking contraption out of one dark corner. Grumps opened one of the cages, dragged out a hulking bull of a dog and pulled it towards the treadmill. As soon as it stepped onto the track the well oiled rollers began to turn. The dog involuntarily stepped forward, first one paw forward and then another. The wheels turned relentlessly. The dog began to trot, and then it ran. Grumps tied the rope round its neck to the stand in front of the dog.

'That's it boy, run as fast as you can. We'll run him for about half an hour. That'll get his stamina up, eh boys? This will be one of your jobs once the dogs get used to you. Go along to the cages, put the backs of your hands out, let 'em smell you. Show no fear; they can sense it. Got to let them know who's master, see?'

Bob and I went along the cages. Wet noses sniffed our outstretched hands. One English bull terrier bitch lay on her side, suckling six of her brood.

'Got to be careful: bull terriers have a tendency to kill their young. Have to keep an eye on her. Don't want her doing any damage.'

'When they've had a litter, how do you know which ones to keep, Grumps?'

'The ones with the biggest button, son.'

I listened intently. Bob scratched his head.

'Buttons, Dad?'

'Bum'oles, boy, bum'oles! Shows they're brave, see? Another thing, if you step forward when they're puppies and they step towards you, you know they're intelligent and brave. If they step backwards, they're cowards and no good to anyone. Drown 'em in the water butt. Don't want to weaken the breed. This world's no place for weaklings and cowards. Same in any world, see? Now look'em straight in the eye. Show no fear.'

'What are their names, Dad?'

'No names, boys. These are killing machines, not pets. Charlie, get that white one out; we'll hang him for an hour or two.'

'What breed is that one, Grumps?'

'English bull terrier. Once they latch on they

never let go ... buggers to shift. Their teeth are incisors. Don't let go till their teeth meet.'

Dad led the white one to another corner and unfurled a thick rope screwed to the roof of the building. He enticed the dog to jump up, teasing it with a loop of the rope. After several tries, the dog leapt and locked on.

'That's it, Charlie, now let 'im 'ang.'

The dog thrashed backwards and forwards, the muscles in its thick neck bulging. Its teeth bared, it hung on about a foot from the ground – no noise, just powerful sweating effort.

'Why has that one got flat teeth?' I asked my dad.

'He's had his fighting and fornicating days. No good to us any more. Filed his teeth down, put him with a young'un; he'll help train the other one up, help him get the blood lust but won't be able to do any damage.'

'You boys, now them cages is empty, clear out all that straw and mess. Then put some fresh hay in and throw the old stuff on the compost heap at the back of the shed.'

'Oh, Dad, do we have to?'

'Do as you're told or I'll clip your ears. Now go on.'

The air outside was refreshing.

'What do you think, Eric? Can't wait to see a fight. Hope they let us.'

'Me too,' I said.

The dog still pounded the treadmill. The white bull just hung there, swinging from side to side.

Hide and Seek

'Quick, June, close the drawer. Don't tell Mum where I am or I'll bash yer.' Not really. I wouldn't hurt my little sis for the world, but I knew it would get her moving.

She obeyed, giving me a leg up into the drawer of the built-in cupboard, the only piece of furniture apart from the three piece suite and fly leaf table in the whole room. Nan's finest glass, locked in the cupboard, rattled on the shelves above me. June slowly closed the long tin drawer, starting to cry as she did so. She left just a tiny gap for me to see out into the room. I loved playing hide and seek. We all did, especially us boys. I often surprised the family by hiding behind the curtains or the back of the settee. Dad always laughed, Mum usually stood with hands on hips, looking stern but smiling. This time they'd never guess where I was. Dad would laugh till he cried.

Mum walked in from the kitchen, rubbing her hands on a tea towel. June sat by the dead fire, still crying.

'What you crying for?'

June just sat there, sobbing. I could imagine Mum, always on a short fuse, starting to go red in the face.

'Shut that crying or I'll give you something to cry for. Now shut it!'

June stopped. She knew better than to carry on.

'Silly, snivelling little girl.' I heard Mum turn and walk back to the kitchen, still rubbing her hands vigorously.

'June, can you hear me?' I whispered with the sound ringing in my ears.

'Oh Eric, come out of there. You'll get us both into trouble. Please.'

Mum poked her head around the door. 'Who you talking to?'

I imagined her eyes darting quickly around the room. June didn't answer.

'Talking to yourself again are you? Well, if that's all you've got to do you can come into the kitchen and help me with the cooking. Your father'll be expecting his dinner when he comes in. Where's Eric?' All this she said without taking a breath.

June still didn't answer. She just got up and followed Mum into the kitchen.

Phew! That was a close one, I thought. I tried not to sneeze in my confined space, knowing that it would be heard all over the house. My nose itched, my ears twitched, my eyes watered from the dust in the drawer.

The smells of Mum's cooking wafted towards me and my tummy started its usual rumble of anticipation. Mum and Nan never let us go short of food, even with all the rationing. Grumps or Dad always came home with something and the women of the family would magic whatever it was into something mouth-watering. A crash and a bang on the butcher's block in the back garden, a handful of salt here, a crunch of pepper there, assorted veg from the garden or allotment, and the steamed, baked or battered whatever-scrag-end became prime steak;

108

pork strips became succulent chops; belly of lamb turned into tasty chops.

For the next hour or so I drifted in and out of sleep, more from boredom than anything else as I waited patiently for Dad to come home. I must have completely dropped off at some point because the next thing I heard was Mum's voice calling out from the kitchen.

'Go and find Eric, June. It's almost teatime. Your father will be home in a minute. We don't want the dinner to get cold.'

I heard the muffled bang of the front door as June pretended to go looking for me, then Dad's worried voice trying to calm Mum as she cried with worry. Dad was home? After all that I hadn't heard him come in.

'Charlie, you'll have to call the police.'

I looked out onto the only piece of the room I could see: a tiny rectangle of peeling wallpaper. My heart beat fast. What had I done? Too late now. Maybe if I stayed hidden until they went to bed, then I could creep out, say sorry for being late home and promise not to do it again.

'Now calm down, Joyce. When was the last time you saw him?'

'Just before I started your dinner ... about an hour and a half ago.'

'Well you know what he's like. He probably took himself off to the forest, playing round the Hollow Ponds,' said Dad.

'I told him dinner was at six o'clock.'

'He's probably lost track of time, still climbing trees. He'll be home when he's hungry.'

Nan and Grumps came in from seeing to the chickens. 'Dinner ready yet, Joyce?'

'We can't find Eric.'

109

'Probably in the forest,' said Grumps.

'No he's not,' piped up Bob. 'I've just come from there with our mates. We didn't see him.'

'I'll go and see if he's in one of the neighbours' houses,' volunteered Dad.

'Good idea,' agreed Grumps. 'I'll go and check over on the bomb site. He might be over there ratting with some of the other boys.'

'Never mind,' said Nan, 'he'll turn up when he's hungry.'

'That's what Charlie said,' retorted Mum. 'Bob, June, go and wash your hands and sit up at the table.'

So June had come back. I heard her start to cry again.

'What's up with her?' asked Nan.

'Don't know; she's been like it all afternoon.'

The family settled down to their tea and the house went quiet. I could hear my heart beating, and my tummy was rumbling uncontrollably. As Dad often said, I could eat the peelings off the potatoes I got so hungry. My confined space now felt more like a coffin than a drawer and I ached all over, my movement severely restricted. I remembered little June sleeping in this very drawer when she was tiny, all wrapped up and warm where Mum could keep an eye on her. With her happy gurgling still a smile in my memory and the warmth of the flickering fire helping me relax, I must have drifted off into a less troubled sleep.

When I woke up the fire was glowing brightly and Grumps was sitting in his armchair with no lights on, just staring into the open fire, drawing heavily on his roll- up. I realised I needed the toilet. I was lying there with a little stiffy, and all I could think of was wanting to do a wee very badly. Suddenly the light went on, blinding me for a second as Dad walked into the room.

'We've searched everywhere again. I've called the police. They're sending someone right away.'

What did they need a policeman for? I wondered if someone had been hurt.

Dad looked at his fob watch. 'It's ten o'clock now.'

I could hear Mum and Nan crying in the kitchen. Great sobs began to ring through the house as they blew their noses simultaneously, sounding like fog horns. Realisation crept into my foggy brain: it's me they're looking for! What could I do now? How was I going to get out of this one? Just then there was a loud knocking on the front door. I heard my dad's feet pounding the floorboards as he went to let in the constable, who hobnailed his way to the parlour.

'Evenin'. What's the trouble exactly?'

'Eric's disappeared.' Grumps became the spokesman for the family.

'He's not been in trouble with the law, has he?' asked Mum.

'No Mrs Joyce, he's just got too much spirit, that's all.'

Panic stricken, I looked out from my hiding place and saw Constable Parkin in his dark blue uniform, bright shiny buttons catching the firelight, helmet held under one arm, and a long menacing truncheon strapped to his side. I feared and respected this community policeman. They all stood there: Mum and Nan, limp hankies in their hands, mascara running down their faces; Dad and Grumps, beer in hand, dejectedly staring into the open fire. Constable Parkin was at least a foot taller than anyone else.

Would I get a smack? Would Mum keep me in for a week? What about my sweet ration? What should I do? I could try every excuse under the sun, but there was no way out now. As Dad and Grumps would say: face up to the action. Be bold! Maybe Dad and Grumps would see the funny side. They would protect me, I knew they would.

Shifting my position, I managed to thread my fingers through the tiny gap. I got a grip on the outside metal frame and tensed my muscles, ready to pull the drawer open. Here we go!

'Boo! It's me!' I announced as I opened the drawer. 'April Fool! Penny for the Guy! Merry Christmas! Surprise!'

'I'll give you a bleedin' surprise!' Dad rushed over, grabbed my ear and pulled me out of the drawer. My other ear went numb as he hit the side of my head. 'April bleedin' fool's day! What do you think you were up to?'

I tried to duck as he hit me again. 'I fell asleep … only just woke up,' I lied.

Mum and Nan just stood there open-mouthed, their large runny eyes staring at me. 'Well, you can go to bed with no tea,' choked Mum.

'Can I do a wee first, I'm bursting.'

'Cheeky little sod,' said Nan.

A great booming laugh erupted from Constable Parkin. 'Well I'll say goodnight then. Wait till I tell the duty sergeant. We'll have a good laugh over this one, I can tell you. Goodnight to you all.' He placed his helmet on top of his giant's head, almost scraping the ceiling. 'Don't be too hard on the boy; he's just got too much spirit.' He cobbled his way to the front door, laughing as he slammed it behind him.

'Eric, get to bed! I'll deal with you in the morning.'

I knew what that meant.

Silent Night

June and I looked at each other knowingly: here we go again. Downstairs, Mum and Dad were having a really bad row, nearly coming to blows. We had no idea what the row was about as we disappeared under the blankets, cuddling each other and crying. The muffled screams and bellowed shouts reached us through the bedclothes. It went on for ages and, eventually, we both fell into an uneasy sleep.

On waking, we were surrounded by a deathly silence and on lifting the bedcovers, we could see nothing in the inky blackness. June reached out, touching my arm.

'I don't like the dark, Eric. Where's our mum?'

'I don't know. Stay there until I find the light switch.' Holding my hands out in front of me, I felt my way along the wall to it. *Click.* Nothing happened. *Click, click.* Still nothing. June began to whimper.

'Don't worry, the shilling meter's probably gone,' I reassured her. I groped my way to the bedroom doorknob. Moonlight from the landing window flooded into our room. 'Wait there, June, I'll go and find Mum.'

Crossing the landing, I went downstairs into the sitting room. Mum sat in her usual chair by the fireside, tears running down her cheeks as she rocked herself backwards and forwards, wringing her hands.

'Mum, you all right?'

'He's gone down the pub,' was all she said.

'Could I have a shilling for the light please, Mum?'

'No, I don't want you seeing me like this. Go to bed.'

'But, Mum, we're hungry and June's frightened of the dark.'

'Do as you're told!' Her voice was nearly hysterical and she began to push herself out of the chair. I'd had enough wallops to know the signs. I shut the lounge door and retreated back up to our sanctuary.

'We've got to stay here, Mum says.'

'But Eric, I'm hungry.'

'I know, I know. When Mum goes to bed, I'll creep down and see what I can find in the kitchen.' I cuddled her, feeling the tension go out of her body and her rhythmic breathing on my cheek as I stroked her chestnut hair and hummed softly to her. She fell asleep in my arms, silent tears flowing down her cheeks, running onto my neck and soaking my shirt. After a little while I eased myself from under her, placed her head on the pillow and covered her up. Every now and then a little sob interrupted her breathing. My tummy rumbled loudly. Why did these things always happen when Nan and Grumps were away on their annual holiday at King's Club on Canvey Island?

After what seemed like forever, I heard Mum come up to her bedroom. I waited for the clock in the hallway to tick away another hour before I crept down to the hall, listened to Mum's soft snores from her and Dad's bedroom, then made a silent dash for the kitchen. My tummy was making so much noise I felt sure Mum would wake. My heart thumped loudly as I took two slices of bread from the breadbin. Opening

114

the cooler cupboard, I scooped two dollops of dripping from the pot with my fingers, then, using my fingers as a knife, I spread the gooey substance over the bread as best as I could. I didn't dare use a knife in case it hit against anything or I dropped it. I retreated, goodies in hand, back up to our bedroom.

Halfway across the darkened landing, 'That you Charlie?' rang out from Mum's room. I stood stock still, sure that the neighbours could hear my heart beating. 'Don't you dare come in here tonight. You can sleep on the settee. Now bugger off!'

Silence. I wanted to cough, sneeze and scratch my arse all at the same time. Instead, I made a quick dash for our room, my heart still pounding. I sat on the bed and munched my bread and dripping. It tasted good. I placed the other slice within reach of June in case she woke up. With nothing else to do, I lay down on the bed.

I woke with the sun pouring into our room. I looked over at June: she was still asleep. The bread and dripping was beginning to curl up at the edges.

'You awake, Eric? It's time to go to school. Wake June.' It was as if she could see through the bedroom door.

'Yes, Mum.'

June opened her eyes. White lines ran down her face where the tears had dried. Throwing the covers off, we both realised we had gone to bed fully clothed. We laughed, brushed ourselves down, trying to get rid of the wrinkles in our clothes, and went down to the kitchen. Mum stood over the stove, stirring our porridge, her hair in curlers held in place by a brightly coloured scarf. She had her pinny wrapped around her, her stockings rolled down to her ankles and her feet encased in bunny slippers that

Dad had made. She tried to hide her red, swollen eyes, but we knew.

'Eat your breakfast, then off you go.'

With that she left us to our own devices. We were used to that.

'How long do you think this one's going to last, Eric?'

'Don't know. The last one lasted three months.'

In the evening, Mum stood at the stove, still red eyed, getting our supper. Dad came home from work, his breath a blast furnace of alcohol.

'Sit at the table. Dinner's ready,' said Mum to the tiled wall.

Holding three hot plates, she roughly plonked Dad's dinner down, spilling some of the gravy onto the table cloth. Dad said nothing. June and I sat with our heads bowed. You could cut the air with a wooden spoon. The meal was eaten in total silence. The only sound was the clink of knives and forks scraping on the plates as we tucked in. Despite everything we never lost our appetites.

'Tell your muvver, I got an important meeting in the morning. Tell 'er I got to be up at seven. Go on, tell 'er.' Dad was a notoriously heavy sleeper, probably as a result of the booze. 'I don't want to be late, see?' He was looking straight at me, his beery breath making my ears curl.

'Mum—' I began.

'I heard. Finish your dinner then go out and play.'

We stayed in the garden until dark. This was mid-September so there was still some warmth in the twilight. We had just carried out one of our duties – locking the chickens safely away in their coop – when Mum called us in.

'Where's Dad?' asked June.

'Gone down the pub. Now go and top and tail yourselves, 'jamas on, then off to bed.'

Next morning Mum woke us a little bit earlier than usual.

'Get dressed. Your breakfast's on the table. I've got to go down the shops; I'll be about an hour.'

As we were getting dressed we heard the front door slam hard. A stirring in the other room told us Dad was just waking up.

'What the bloody hell is going on?'

We could hear him crashing about and sat down on the bed, staying quiet to keep out of his way.

'Bloody woman, what does she think she's playing at? I'll murder her when I get dressed. Joyce! Come here, you bitch!'

Silence. Then we heard him hopping around the room trying to put on his trousers, followed by heavy boots.

'Bloody woman! JOYCE!' He flung the bedroom door open, the handle crashing into the wall. 'JOYCE!' His heavy footsteps thundered through the building. 'Joyce, where the bloody hell are you? I'm late.' There was no answer. 'I'll see to her later.'

The front door crashed shut and Dad's motorbike revved into life. He was gone. June and I sighed with relief, enjoying the silence.

'Come on,' I said, 'let's go and eat our breakfast.'

I opened our bedroom door and looked out. June stood behind me holding onto my hand.

'It's all clear.'

Dad's and Mum's bedroom door was wide open. I looked in. Something was pinned to one of the pillows – a note. Curiosity got the better of me. I crept

into their private room and cocked my head sideways
to read it: *Get up you lazy bastard, it's seven o'clock.*
I laughed out loud, all tension leaving me.

Saturday Morning Pictures

Saturday mornings were my dream time away from the family and the hustle and bustle of everyday life. They were spent at the Century cinema at Bakers Arms, Leyton, a penny bus ride away from home.

Sixpence each, nine thirty kick-off, an orderly queue and no pushing or shoving. Many of us clutched our brown paper bags of sweets, the rustling a sure sign that we were too impatient – the temptation too great – to wait for the 'flicks' to start. All around the crunching of home-made toffee or nut crunch – 'jaw breakers' we used to call them – could be heard. Some kids had penny gobstoppers: golf ball size things, with an aniseed right in the middle – difficult to get into your mouth. Others had home-made sugar mice with beady eyes made from silver balls, the only inedible parts being the candle string tails. Other favourites were Spanish sticks, chewy tiger nuts, sherbet dabs and flying saucers. The saucers were coloured rice paper with fizzy orange or lemon flavoured sherbet inside; the rice paper would melt on your tongue and the released sherbet would fizz, going up your nose and making your eyes water. This would invariably be followed by a fit of sneezing or coughing.

With our refreshments sorted, and mostly eaten, we started what we kids called the 'sixpenny shuffle'. Shunting along, clutching our sticky sixpences, we eventually got to the kiosk window.

119

'One seat, please.'

Seating was a free for all – no regimentation in those days. If the seats were all full we had to stand at the back – health and safety not even heard of. Take their money and cram 'em in. Despite that, we'd usually find a seat, turning round to look for school chums, waving and shouting hellos. The usherette's crisp black and white uniform made her stand out from the crowd. Her tray was balanced on one hip, the battery operated strip light swaying as she walked up the aisles. The tray bulged with pop corn, lollies, ice cream and chocolate. This was not for us; only the rich kids could afford them.

When the auditorium lights began to dim, a rising crescendo of noise made the floor tremble. The organ slowly rose up in front of the silver screen. Tunes I cannot remember now bellowed out and the organist smiled majestically, his head turned halfway round to face his audience as his fingers flashed across the keys. The screen lit up with the words of the songs, and the sing-a-long began: *Show me the way to go home. I'm tired and I want to go to bed...* A bouncing ball hopped from one word to the other, making us keep pace with the music. After several songs, the organ with its flashing lights and the organist with his flashing teeth began to disappear down into the pit once more. The screen lit up again as loud music assailed our ears. Pearl and Dean adverts flashed up, all for local shops and restaurants. No one took any notice of these; we were too busy throwing half eaten sweets and paper at each other. The ushers tried desperately to keep us in order, until the house lights would come on and the cinema manager would march manfully onto the stage.

'If you lot don't quieten down and behave, there'll be no more pictures, so BE-HAVE!'

After his threats, all would go quiet again, the lights would slowly dim and the film show would begin – all in black and white. First, Edgar Lustgarten – drum roll, please! – the former Scotland Yard chief inspector who would narrate a crime that had taken place in London, Liverpool or wherever, perpetrated by dastardly criminals and murderers who were apprehended by their own greed and incarcerated forever. It kept me on the straight and narrow for quite some time.

Then the real fun began. Cartoons! Mickey Mouse and friends, Donald Duck and Pluto, spinach-eating Pop-Eye and his girlfriend Olive Oil, (The school boy joke making the rounds at that time was: *How do you stop your todger from going rusty? Stick it in Olive Oil.* Ha!Ha!), and, of course, Bluto the bully. The boys all booed him.

After that, we might get Flash Gordon. Only four minutes to defeat the inscrutable Ming with the evil eyes and save the world. Flash would always save the world – and the swooning girls in the cinema. Another time it would be the Three Stooges, Abbot and Costello or Laurel and Hardy. We knew one of them would get a slap, which never failed to make us laugh. Roy Rogers and Trigger was another favourite. He would always give us a song before he shot a 'baddie'. Other weeks it would be the Lone Ranger with Tonto, his Indian friend who called him Kimo Sabi and always said the bad men spoke with 'forked tongue'. Best of all was Superman. We always had to wait till the next week to find out what happened to him. A whole week was so frustrating; it seemed as if Saturday would never come. And who could forget Lassie, man's best friend. She would always save the good guys. Not everyone knew that sometimes Lassie was a boy dog. They used to strap a furry cod piece

121

onto the unfortunate animal; although it probably kept him warm when he leapt into the water to save someone.

After all the sweets and Nan's homemade lemonade, I would need a wee halfway through the show. You had to put your hand up in the dark, hoping one of the ushers would spot you and take you. There was one particular occasion when I'd had my hand up for five minutes, waving my arm about frantically. I was desperate. I sat there squeezing my 'liquorice allsorts' until there was no option but to make a dash for it. Needless to say someone caught me before I got there.

'Where are you going?'

'I need a pee.' I hopped from one foot to the other.

'Why did you leave your seat without permission?'

'I had my hand up for five minutes. Nobody came.'

'Well, I didn't see you.'

The big bully usher came and stood right by the exit to the toilet. Urgency overtaking expediency, I crashed straight into him, my right hand squeezing my 'liquorice'. Desperately, I charged into the loo. Too late. The amber liquid was already running down my leg, soaking my woollen socks and filling my shoes. Mum would kill me. I went into one of the cubicles and locked the door, looking around for something to soak up the wet. I knew the toilet paper would be no good: it was the council stuff, shiny and bright, as stiff as cardboard and twice as lethal. It made great paper planes, but was no good at all for your bum. Or for patting out wet trousers, socks and shoes. I decided to use my pants. When I got home I could always tell Mum that I'd forgotten to put any on.

Taking my wet smelly trousers and pants off, I removed my soggy socks and shoes and tried in vain to squeeze them dry. Just then the bully boy usher burst into the toilets. Seeing the cubicle shut, he banged on the door.

'What yer doing in there, havin' a wank?'

'N-no,' I stammered.

'Well 'urry up, you've been in there ages.'

'Won't be a mo',' I called back, stamping on my pants with my socks under them, trying to squeeze all the wet out. All logic had deserted me and panic was beginning to set in. I lifted the lid and went to throw my soggy pants down the loo. There, staring back at me, was a 'floater'. Just my luck. That meant that the loo didn't flush properly. Stuffing my pants in after it, I desperately pulled the chain, willing it to flush. All I got was a gurgle and an empty chamber. Embarrassment and perspiration broke out at the same time. *Pleeease!* Again I pulled desperately at the chain. Nothing happened. Bully boy was still standing outside.

'Now I know why they call these WCs,' he said wryly. 'Wankers Club! Come on, open up.'

I was still naked from the waist down. Trying desperately to pull my socks on while they were still wet was proving an almost impossible task. Next came my short trousers, up and around my waist, shirt tail half in and half out. I had one last desperate pull at the chain. Nothing happened. There was only one thing left to do. Holding my breath and closing my eyes I inserted my hand down the loo. Wrapping my pants around the floater, I pushed the whole lot round the bend and out of sight. My shirt and jumper sleeve were soaking. *Bugger it!* I slid back the engaged bolt and stepped out.

123

'Bloody hell, kid, you been havin' a bath in there or what?'

'No, I slipped over in the wet,' I said defensively.

'You must've rolled over a few times as well. *Phaw!* What's that smell? Aftershave? Get on back to yer seat.'

I dodged around him, entering the darkened cinema relieved that no one could see me. Every eye was on the screen. My wet trousers were beginning to chafe the insides of my legs. I could feel the stinging increasing with every step. Finally I made it back to my seat. I sat very still, making out I was watching the film. I couldn't wait for it to end so that I could sneak out just before the national anthem and the lights going on. I could hear whispers in the row behind me.

''Ere 'arry, can you smell piss?'

'Yeah, some dirty bastard must've done it in the last show. If I catch 'im, I'll tear 'is ears off.'

I slid out of my seat, crawled to the nearest exit and was away.

Saturday Night Market

'You've all got to be in bed early tonight; we've got some men coming round for a game of cards,' said Grumps. 'Don't want you kids under our feet.'

'Not me,' I said. 'Nan wants me to go with her down the market.'

'Well if you're going, Bob can go too,' said Grumps. 'Take a sack each, one of you either side of the high street.'

This was sometimes a Saturday treat for me. With jigger (or go-cart as the Yanks called it) and sacks, we would step out into the moonlight that we normally only saw through our bedroom window. Excitement beckoned. With no fridges or freezers, the butchers, fruit vendors and flower sellers, bellowing their wares, tried to sell off their perishable goods on a Saturday night, knowing they would not keep until opening time on Monday.

We all heard the whoosh as Aunt Vera plonked the first lot of chips into the deep, red-hot lard. She was cooking our evening meal of egg and chips and I licked my lips as the smell of frying wafted round the kitchen.

The meal over, I rubbed my tummy and watched June and Christine rub their eyes. With the roaring fire and full bellies, I knew they would be heading for bed very soon. Stifling a yawn, I asked if I could leave the table. I needed some cold fresh air.

Bob followed me to the front door. The moon, half hidden by racing clouds, shone down on us and stars twinkled. The only car in the street was parked about half way down, its rear reflectors blinking as the moon went in and out. The cold night air revived me.

'Can't wait till we get down the market, El.' Bob's voice rose excitedly and I could see his cold breath.

'You betcha, Bob,' I said.

Nan called us back inside. 'Come on boys, get your glad rags on. It's almost time to leave.'

You could hear the high street before you got to it: all the stallholders calling out their wares made a loud but familiar noise. 'Spivs' on the edge of the market would be selling their wares without a licence, one eye shifting from side to side, looking for the 'toby' – the man in charge of the market – or the pointed helmet of the street bobby. If they saw one of them coming they would quickly stuff whatever they were selling into large suitcases, turn their collars up and hats down, hunch their shoulders and disappear into the crowd. The stallholders didn't mind these men as long as they weren't selling anything they themselves were trading. 'Live and let live' was everyone's motto at that time. Besides, it added character and colour to the market.

Overhead lights turned night into day and every stall had a paraffin lamp to help display their wares. The glow from the scene lit up the side streets; it was so bright you almost needed sunglasses. You could buy anything from a pin to a white elephant – literally. If one stallholder didn't have what you wanted, he had a cousin or an uncle a quarter of the way down the street who would be able to oblige. If not, come back next week and there was your white elephant or whatever, waiting for you, dung and all.

There were two flea pit cinemas on the high street. Tickets ranged from half a crown up in the 'gods', where all the snogging took place, or two shillings downstairs at the back – the darkest part where all the groping took place. The front stalls, where all the people who actually wanted to watch the film sat, were eleven pence.

About halfway down the street was a music hall, laughter forever seeping through the wall into the old Anglican church next door, its steeple reaching towards heaven. The two buildings were not entirely compatible, pious sobriety and laughter being a strange combination, but nobody seemed to mind.

Further down on the left was Manzie's pie and mash shop, selling steak pies and mash with green liquor (made from potato, parsley and seasoning) and chilli vinegar with a side order of steamed eels. That was my favourite. As you entered, there was a long marble-topped counter where I just held up my hands with my money because I couldn't see over it. 'One pie and mash please.' Someone usually leaned over the counter to see who was there.

Aluminium knives and forks clinked on stoneware plates. Then people scraped away with spoons, getting the last residue of green liquor. Condensation ran down the black and white tiled walls. Huge fans whirred on heavily embossed ceilings as moisture dripped onto the heads of chomping customers. Black and white marble slabs covered the floor. There were no tables and chairs as such: mighty high-backed black pews marched in line down the whole length of the room beside tables of elongated white marble slabs held up on wrought iron legs. The building had been standing since the reign of Queen Victoria and reminded me a little of a church.

'More liquor,' the shop girls would shout out

to the kitchen. Why they shouted, nobody knew, because they had a buzzer code that could be heard all over the shop: one buzz for liquor, two for pies, three for mashed spuds and so on. Anyway, a bald headed man would appear from the kitchen, a chrome bucket in each hand, steam from the green contents surrounding him. 'Mind your backs, please.' He weaved his way between the pews.

Two buzzes sounded. 'More pies please.' Another man would appear, a long metal tray extending in front of him, a leather apron stopping the hot metal from burning his stomach and a piece of hessian sacking protecting his hands; crusty pies fresh from the oven steamed their way behind the liquor man.

'Form queues please – this one to take away, this one for eating in.'

The great chrome and brass tills trilled majestically. It was organised chaos. The green liquor was poured into large chrome cauldrons; metal ladles slurped the liquid onto pies and mash – the mash scraped onto the side of the plate, and the pies golden and hot.

'Do you want chilli vinegar?' a shop girl would ask before drizzling the brown liquid on top of the whole sumptuous meal.

The customers, queuing out of the front door and part way down the street waited patiently for their turn, tummies rumbling with happy anticipation.

Their plates scraped clean, people would leave their seats to rejoin the long queues for 'afters', a pudding, a dessert – call it what you will – of juicy, rust-coloured rhubarb or apple pies, no custard, just a shake of castor sugar over the top.

Up the street from Manzie's, with all its lights ablaze, stood the shop selling pease pudding (yellow

128

split peas, soaked in water for twenty four hours and then boiled into submission until they melted in one), saveloys (elongated sausage, turned on the skillet to a succulent golden orange) and faggots. These were all served on greaseproof plates with small, flat wooden spoons. With salt and pepper to taste – lovely! The mouth watering aromas steamed around the shop and out of the door. The display window always misted over with condensation, droplets of water racing each other down the glass panes. I once saw two inebriated men, swaying side to side on the pavement, watching two drops about to descend and betting half crowns on which one would slide down and reach the window seal first.

As they waited in line, women's seamed stockings wilted in the moist atmosphere and sawdust muffled the sound of the men's hobnail boots on the floor. The manager wore a straw boater set at a jaunty angle and a grin to match his handlebar moustache. The sleeves of his white coverall were held back with expanding silver armbands above the elbow, and a stiffly starched blue-striped apron completed the ensemble. 'Next please!'

Outside, on an open stall, eels wriggled in over-sized zinc trays. People stood in line there too.

'Four of your best eels please.'

'Certainly, sir.'

A knife would flash, and we would watch fascinated as one after the other the fishmonger cut the heads off the poor creatures. Decapitated though they were, they continued to wriggle from side to side. Placing the gutting knife where their heads had been, the fishmonger would split the eel from head, or rather neck to tail with one deft stroke. Turning the knife over, he would run the blunt edge over the eel's body once more, removing all the guts and bits and deftly flicking them off the board into a zinc bucket at his green-wellied feet. He would then cut the cleaned eels into bite sized chunks and wrap the whole lot in newspaper. Wiping the knife on a cloth by his side and sponging all the red blood into another bucket, he would then pick up his steel and lovingly sharpen his trusted knife. 'Next order please.'

My favourite stall stood outside one of the cinemas. The silver and brass sarsaparilla machine looked just the same as a beer pump, except there was a nozzle for cold sarsaparilla and one for hot. The pump oozed out the brown frothy liquid that had an unusual taste. I liked it. When I was small, I couldn't get my mouth round the whole word and I called it 'sarsaprella'.

The few fish and chip shops always did a roaring trade. When I was given a treat, I would go in and get a penny worth of 'crackle' – all the little bits of batter that had spit off in the hot cooking fat. The chip man put it all to one side in his hot display cabinet and people who could afford it often had cod, chips and a penny worth of this batter.

The Pearly King and Queen frequently passed along the waiting queues. 'Spare a ha'penny or a farthing for your local hospital.' People fiddled in their pockets looking for small change, often with rolled towels under their arms and hair still damp from the swimming baths or the Turkish steam room and slipper baths opposite. The imposing edifice of the municipal bath house squatted on Victorian columns with many steps leading up to it. I knew what went on inside, having experienced it many times. There were about a dozen cubicles, white tiled from floor to ceiling, each containing a six foot cast iron bath tub. Wooden seats lined one wall, their timber scrubbed to bleached whiteness, and steam billowed out over the cubicle walls while you sat waiting your turn and listening to the banter of the bathroom attendants in their white uniforms. They all held large chrome keys in their hands.

'Number three's free, mate.'

'Can I have some more 'ot in number nine? The water's bleedin' freezin' in 'ere.'

'You've got five minutes left.'

'Don't be so bloody cheeky or I'll throw a bucket of cold water over you.'

On this Saturday night we watched the Pearly King and Queen shuffle along the queue and then disappear into the crowd.

'Come on,' said Nan, 'time for you boys to go to work. I'll meet you outside the butcher's at the bottom of the high street at 10 o'clock.'

Bob and I split up, heading for the top of the street – him one side, me the other. He gave me a good luck thumbs up sign and then, sacks in hand, we disappeared under the first stalls. The idea of gleaning under the stalls was to help the family budget – as long as we didn't get caught – and anything dropped there was fair game for us kids. Into the sack went bruised apples and pears, squashed tomatoes, potatoes, cabbage leaves – anything that was edible. We travelled the length of the street, seeing only people's legs and feet shuffling along with the crowd.

When my bag was full to the brim, I emerged from under the stalls and staggered under the weight down a side street and then a narrow alley, where we had hidden our jigger behind an old shed. Bob was already there retrieving our pride and joy. Our version was an upside down orange crate with one side cut off; this was nailed to a plank about six feet long by twelve inches wide and as thick as you could get it; twelve inch fixed wheels sawn off a rusty old perambulator – probably from some bombsite or other – were permanently fixed under the plank with bent nails, straightened and hammered in; two six inch wheels (hopefully from the same pram) were bolted at the front through the middle of the axle, through the plank and held in place by a large nut and washer; a piece of rope, cut from the end of Mum's washing line, was tied each side as close to the wheels as possible.

(In jigger racing, this sophisticated steering mechanism – a looped rope held in each hand – enabled us to steer left or right. Sometimes, if the front axle was long enough we could also steer with our feet. Stopping was another matter: feet down, shoes placed firmly on the pavement, sparks flying from our heels, we'd slowly bring the thing to a standstill. Mum quickly learnt why my shoes were thin and scuffed. Down the cobbler's she went, coming back with brown paper bag in one hand, hammer in the other. Bang, bang bang. Steel toe and heel studs, plus all the studs in between. I could tap dance like Gene Kelly and Fred Astaire rolled into one. I loved the crunch as I walked along.)

Placing both sacks on the jigger we set off for the bottom of the high street, which wasn't easy as we kept getting in people's way.

'Let's go down Palmerston Road and cut through the back doubles until we get to the bottom,' I suggested.

Bob nodded. We were only half way down when we left the comfort of the many lights. It became dark and quiet except for a few people making their way home.

'Want an apple, Bob?'

'Why not? Let's stop and have a munch. We've got plenty of time; it's only quarter past nine.'

Sitting on top of the sacks, we munched away.

Suddenly Bob started coughing and spluttering.

'Ugh, that's horrible!' He spat bits of apple on to the ground.

I looked at him, surprised. 'What's up?'

'I just bit a maggot in half,' he said, rubbing his tongue with his cuff.

'That's lucky,' I laughed.

'What do you mean it's lucky?' he asked, still spitting and rubbing his tongue.

I laughed again. 'Well, it's lucky it's not me.'

The next thing I knew, the other half of his apple was hitting me square between the eyes, knocking me off my sack and landing me flat on my back. The breath was squeezed from my body.

'Now that's what I call a lucky shot.' Bob couldn't stop laughing.

I was too winded to do anything about it. The bones in my back ached where I had struck the pavement. 'I'll get you another time,' I said, catching my breath. 'Now come on, Nan will be waiting for us at the butcher's.'

We set off once more with the jigger wheels squealing their protest at the weight they had to carry.

'You wait here with this lot and I'll go and help with the meat,' Bob instructed when we reached the bottom of the high street.

'No, let's hide the jigger. I want to come with you.'

We hid the laden jigger behind a wall at the end of the street opposite Coppermill lane and set off for the butcher's. On the way we poked our heads around the door of the Old Cock Tavern to have a gander at the grown-ups' antics. The old music hall upright piano rocked backwards and forwards, the enthusiasm of the grinning pianist infectious, and beer spilled from pints propped up on top of it. Warmth and well-being poured out of the open doorway and windows. One man threw an empty packet of cigarettes out of a window – non-filtered *Weights;* only women smoked cigarette with filters. Everyone began to sing along with the pianist, *When England Invaded Germany, Hitler's Troops Surrendered.* My dad had told me what the words really stood for:

> *...Bye bye blackbird.*
> *There she was in the woods,*
> *Taking off her lover's shirt.*
> *Bye bye blackbird.*
> *Then he laid her on the grass,*
> *Stuck his finger up her arse.*
> *Bye bye blackbird.*
> *No one else could love or understand her.*
> *Oh, what hard luck stories they all hand her.*
> *Pack your bag and light the light,*
> *I'll be home late tonight.*
> *Blackbird bye bye...*

We made our way on up the mile and a quarter stretch of market and reached the butcher's just as he flung open the shop window.

'Ladies, the auction will begin in three minutes.'

His assistant placed all the meat on the white marble slab: hefty chunks of beef, pork, lamb shanks, sausages, liver, kidneys, hearts, pigs' heads and trotters – you name it, it was there. We pushed through the crowd, knowing Nan would be at the front. She would have been there for at least an hour. This was no ordinary auction. The butcher shouted out what price he wanted for a particular piece of meat: 'Now who will give me 2/6d for this side of pork?' The first one to put his or her hand up got the prize.

Nan always bought offal and brisket, heart and liver. She could only afford the cheap cuts. But between them, she, Mum and Aunt Vera always produced food fit for a king: stews with steaming dumplings, braised liver and onions, mountains of potatoes from our sacks and delicious soups made from all the potato peelings, greens or whatever vegetables we had gleaned.

With shopping bags full of meat, we all set off home. The October chill crept into our bones as we trudged down the high street. Nan stopped abruptly, opened her purse and smiled down at us.

'Fancy a lemonade and an arrowroot biscuit?'

''Cor, yeah, Nan!'

'You'll have to sit outside. Don't let the bags of food out of your sight. I'm going to have a gin and orange.' She licked her lips in anticipation.

The singing in the Old Cock Tavern was still going strong. It echoed down the darkened street as Nan opened the door and entered the brightly lit pub.

An hour later we trudged home, burping lemonade.

Bonfires

'Quick, El, grab that piece of wood out of the stream; it'll do for the bonfire.'

'Naw, it's wet.'

'Don't matter, put it in the jigger.'

The excitement grew as the day progressed. Tonight was bonfire night. Penny bangers were stuffed under my pillow back at home, ready for later. We were going to burn an effigy of Guy Fawkes, the man who had been involved in the Gunpowder Plot, the conspiracy to assassinate James I in 1604. Good old Guy. Patrick and I had our own Guy, and in true British tradition had been standing outside Woolworths on Walthamstow High Street for two weeks, chanting 'penny for the Guy, penny for the Guy,' rusty old cocoa tin in hand (taken from the dustbin, label removed). The Guy, poor thing, was Nan's jumper and her old long drawers, both 'borrowed' off the washing line and stuffed with newspaper and straw commandeered from the compost heap. Rabbit droppings fell out if we shook him, only smelling slightly of bunny wee. Into it had gone paper and straw, straw and paper, until knickers and jumper were fully stuffed. We had a blown up balloon for its head. Two balloons had already been lost in the process: press too hard trying to paint a face on and - bang! His battered straw hat, we had nicked from the allotment. The scarecrow wouldn't miss it

137

and our need was greater than his. My shoes, positioned at the ends of Nan's knicker legs, finished the job. He was propped up in our jigger, and we had got him to the high street with one of us steering and the other pushing, until the one pushing ran out of breath. 'Change over?' we'd shout with a wheeze.

So, we were standing outside Woolworths on a piece of cardboard jingling the cocoa tin, feet turning blue, when up came two boys a couple of school years ahead of us, their sorry looking Guy in tow. We'd seen them in the playground at dinner time.

'This is our pitch,' they said menacingly.

'No it's not. We've been here for two weeks. Ain't that right, Patrick?'

Patrick nodded, panic in his eyes. He stepped behind me, knowing I would protect him.

'Well it's ours now.'

They grabbed our jigger and pushed it out of the way. The poor old Guy fell out and yet another balloon-head went bang. They laughed. Going bright red and with fists clenched, I felt myself losing control. Before I had time to think, I lashed out, catching the bigger boy on the side of his nose. Blood splashed his would-be accomplice. Jumping up onto their jigger and wading in with fists and feet flying, I demolished their sorry looking 'Guy Fawkes'.

'Now bugger off,' I said, fists still clenched and feet sore.

'No need to be like that,' said the one still holding his nose, the other rubbing his knees. 'We were only joking.'

I grabbed their Guy's head, which was a plastic football, and tucked it under my arm. 'That's mine now; you broke ours. I'll see you in the playground, you try anything else, see!'

My toes began to throb. I'd forgotten I wasn't

wearing shoes. Looking down I saw torn socks and bloodied toes. My knuckles were scraped and raw and I began to hurt. The pain came in waves. I jumped up and down trying to relieve the agony, my bum going *sixpence, half a crown, sixpence, half a crown.* I began to get control. Show no pain, fear or tears: that's what I'd been taught.

'You were a lot of bleedin' good, Patrick!'

'Don't swear. I'll tell yer mum.'

'No you won't or I'll bash yer.'

We picked up our jigger and straightened poor old Guy out. I placed the plastic football head, still grinning stupidly back at me, on Nan's jumper, replaced the straw hat and forced my painful feet back into my shoes. Guy would have to go shoeless for a while. 'Penny for the Guy, mister?'

Jingle jangle. We ran home pulling the jigger behind us, old Fawky bouncing around all over the place. On the way, I got a posy for Mum from the gypsy woman selling her flowers up and down the high street. 'God bless yer, sonny, cross me palm with silver and luck will be yours for ever.' We ran on.

'What's the time?'

'Dunno,' said Patrick. 'I never could tell the time wivout a watch.'

I was always late. Dad would skin me alive. This time I was sucking my knuckles as we ran. I skidded round the corner, home in sight, and said goodbye to Patrick. Pennies jangling in my pocket, I called hello to all the neighbours as I raced by. Opening the garden gate, I hastily pulled the cart through, pushed it under the privet hedge out of sight from the road and took the door key, tied to my trousers with a piece of string, out of my pocket.

'Hurry up Eric, you're late,' said Nan when I got in.

139

I flung the back room door open. Mum, Dad and all the rest of the family were seated around the bare wooden table.

'You're late again,' said Dad.

'Sorry, Dad, couldn't get away from people trying to give me pennies for the Guy. Sorry Mum.' I gave her the posy, smiling innocently, hoping it would work on her.

The excitement tangible, we wrapped up warm that night: welly boots, scarves and gloves – fingerless for me because it was easier to pick up the bangers that way if they were thrown in my direction: I could throw them back while they were still fizzing. We walked down our road, Brook Road, June and I holding Mum's and Dad's hands. As we walked, other families emerged from dimly lit doorways and we exchanged a few greetings on the way.

'Stay together,' said Dad as we neared the crowd at the end of the road and ran ahead.

I tightened my grip on June's hand.

'Eric, I don't like the bangers, they make me frightened.' Little June squeezed my hand.

'Don't worry, I'll look after you. If you get frightened, stand behind me.'

We headed for the noise and could just make out 'Guy Fawkes' on top of the huge bonfire in the middle of the bomb site. A giant effigy in a big black hat, he was stuffed from head to toe, adorned in a red suit with big black buttons running down the tunic, red trousers and big black boots. He looked more like Father Christmas than Guy Fawkes, but we knew it was a mouldy old soldier's uniform from somebody's attic. He sat on top of old railway sleepers, rolls of lino, tree trunks and planks of wood with sawdust from the sawmill down the road thrown in between all of it, easy to catch alight. In fact, anything that would burn and was not nailed down was on that bonfire.

All the boys in the area had tied their own Guys lower down the bonfire, my Guy higher than most as I'd taken him earlier. All around, mums and nans suddenly recognised bits of clothing that had gone missing two weeks earlier. A few clouts could be heard amongst the gathering crowds, the boys not quick enough to duck.

I stood with Dad in the front, June and Mum behind, a two-and-sixpenny box of fireworks at my feet. Inside were rockets, Catherine wheels, jumping crackers (my favourite after bangers), Roman candles and sparklers, although I wouldn't be seen dead with a sparkler – girlie stuff. The girls would wave them around when they were alight, making little patterns in the dark. I had two shillings worth of penny bangers in my pocket, held together with an elastic band, and, best of all, three tuppenny bangers in my inside pocket. The Double Banger! I would save those till last.

The excitement grew as Mr Blake arrived. He was the owner of the local hardware shop and every year he donated two gallons of paraffin. This would get the festivities off with a whoosh. He walked around the fire, sloshing the stuff liberally, soaking everything evenly, then stood back and admired his handiwork. The women scurried forward, baking potatoes in their hands. Digging with one hand, they shoved the large potatoes as near to the fire as they thought wise. Four men stepped up, throwing lighted tapers onto the fire to get the blaze going. It took quickly and the heat became unbearable. Everyone stepped back. A large roll of old lino caught. Becoming engulfed in flame it started to spit hot tar out of the fire. Black globules landed on the grass, smouldering.

Someone put a milk bottle on the ground and placed a rocket inside. 'Stand back,' he warned, lighting the blue touch paper. As the rocket fizzed the force of it knocked the bottle sideways. Someone screamed, 'Watch out!' Everyone turned to look at the fizzing firework. 'Look out!'

The rocket left the milk bottle with a great flurry of sparks, heading straight for the crowd. Everyone ducked as it sped just over their heads, zoomed into a front door on the opposite side of the street and exploded with a loud bang. Sulphur permeated the air as the front door opened.

'Who is it? Any of you kids playing 'knock down ginger'?' said old man Kipper, the most miserable person in the street.

The crowd laughed, relieved that no one was injured.

'Bloody kids,' said the old man, and slammed the front door shut again.

'Miserable old git' said one of the men.

'Watch out!'

I ducked instinctively as a penny banger whizzed past my ear. 'Cor, that was close.' It exploded behind me with a bang.

The fire roared and old 'Guy Fawkes' began to smoulder around the edges. His damp, red jacket was green with mildew; the smell wafting from it was like smelly old socks and steaming Brussels sprouts.

'There he goes,' said Dad.

I looked up, my face beaming in the firelight. Groans, crackles and hissing steam all escaped from the mound of burning timbers and rubbish. The Guy's hat caught alight and his head started to resemble a Roman candle. Everyone cheered. A huge spark puffed from the centre, travelling in a wide arc towards me. I watched, fascinated, as it landed in slow motion right in the centre of my two and sixpenny box of fireworks. I was too slow. The touch paper of one of my favourites spluttered into life. I reached down, trying to retrieve it. Sparks from the offending cracker touched others: Roman candles, Mountain volcanoes. Two weeks of pennying for the Guy outside Woolies erupted right in front of me as Dad grabbed me by the scruff of my neck and pulled me backwards.

'Bad luck, son.'

Patrick came running over towards us. 'Cor, that was good, El! Never seen so many fireworks go off at one time. Magic!'

I stood there despondently.

'Never mind, son, all part of the fun, see?' Dad cuffed my head affectionately.

With no thought of possible danger, I reached into my inside pocket, reassuring myself that my tuppenny bangers were safe. My left hand dived into my jacket pocket; my other bangers were also still there. June cowered behind Mum's skirt, Dad coaxing her out with the promise of a sparkler.

'Hold it out in front of you, there's a good girl.' He lit it with a sliver of wood which glowed fiercely in the breeze. 'Now wave it around a bit.'

June started to make a figure of eight pattern until it spluttered and died. 'Finished, Dad.'

'Well throw it away then.'

It still glowed with red hot metal as she dropped it … straight down her welly boot. She began to cry with pain. Grumps rushed up, beer in hand, and poured the whole pint into her welly.

'There, girlie, that will stop it.'

June stopped crying.

'Take your boot off, love, careful now.'

143

June's soggy sock appeared from the boot. Grumps reached inside, plucking out the dowsed black sparkler. I watched, eyes on stalks, amazed at what I guessed my grandfather was about to do: he put the boot to his lips and drank, his Adam's apple working up and down. Then he wiped the froth from his lips with the back of his hand.

'Waste not, want not,' he grinned.

June retreated behind Mum's skirt again, holding her wet foot off the ground.

I took a penny banger from my pocket and lit it, holding it until it began to fizz before throwing it towards the family I liked the least: the Wozzys, a dirty family with ten kids, all needing a good scrub.

'Watch out!'

They parted as the penny banger hit the ground and exploded.

'Who threw that?' asked Daddy Wozzy, looking around.

Everyone sniggered. Someone else lobbed another banger in their direction. Mummy Wozzy jumped in the air, all eighteen stone of her. As she wobbled back to earth and planted her feet firmly back on the ground, her cami-knickers ended up around her ankles.

'Father, we're going home,' she screeched with embarrassment. She took one foot out of her camis and flicked them towards the fire with her other ham-like leg. Instantly they caught alight.

'Cor, talk about the burning bush,' someone called out.

Mummy Wozzy and brood walked out of the firelight into the darkness.

'Good riddance to bad rubbish!' came from the crowd.

'Spuds are ready!'

144

The women stepped forward, holding their hands up to shield their faces from the heat. Grabbing discarded sticks, they deftly flicked the potatoes away from the fire, rolling them with their feet towards their families. The warm smell of the burning wood, mingled with the steaming, crispy, blackened spuds, wafted over me irresistibly.

'Help yourselves, but let them cool down for a bit, otherwise you'll burn yourselves,' said Mum.

'I'm hungry, Mum.'

'Don't worry Eric, you'll get your share.'

Meanwhile bangers, rockets and jumping jack crackers were going off all over the bomb site. The men swigged beer, laughing, froth oozing out of the tops of their bottles. The clink of glasses vied with the noise of the fireworks. The women sipped their gin, Mum's tipple watered down with a little lime, Nan's topped up with orange borrowed from her weekly allowance from the NHS. As old 'Guy Fawkes' was reduced to smouldering ash, some of the inner timbers of the fire collapsed, sending showers of sparks into the night sky.

Dad picked up a potato, tossing it from hand to hand. 'Blimey, that's 'ot.' He took out his penknife and sliced the potato in two, steam escaping from its thick skin. He held the two halves intact, the white pulp gleaming in the firelight. 'June, Eric, grab a piece. Don't burn yourselves, it's pretty hot.'

The taste was wonderful, all fluffy and earthy, with lashings of margarine melting into the spud.

People quietened down, some standing around, others sitting on broken walls or collapsed chimney stacks. They began to yawn and stretch from the lateness of the hour, the beer, the gin and the warmth from the glowing fire. June lay across Mum's legs, fast asleep.

'I think it's about time we went home.' Dad grabbed June and threw her across his shoulders. She didn't stir. 'Come on, son, it's time for bed.' He took me by the hand. 'We'll wash you in the morning; a little bit of smoke won't hurt you.'

'Yes, Dad.' I didn't argue. I was dead on my feet. I put my blackened hand in his, black tears from the smoking bonfire staining my cheeks. My clothes smelt like a dead ashtray. Mum followed on behind and we trudged up the hill towards home.

'Can we do it again next year?'

''Course we can, son.'

'Thanks, Dad.'

Grumps' Special Recipe

Bob, June, Chris and I were sitting at the kitchen table, tearing newspaper into small squares ready for the privy. Bob and I tore while the girls threaded onto hemp string with a meat skewer. With enough paper threaded, one of us would cut the string and tie it with a slip knot, ready to hang on the rusty nail in the outhouse. I always folded the famous faces inwards: I didn't like the thought of wiping my bum on them. Nor did Grumps, unless it was Attlee or Churchill; he didn't like politicians. He had a little ditty he sang when he sat on the loo, which never failed to amuse me. 'Here he goes again,' Nan would say when Grumps's dulcet tones came booming from the outside privy: *Well bless my soul, I've wiped my hole on a little bit of tissue paper.*

'You boys finished that tearing yet?'

'Nearly, Dad,' said Bob.

'Well, when you've finished, come into the scullery and I'll show you how to make my special beer for Christmas.'

Bob and I quickly finished the last bundle.

'Can we leave the table, please Nan?'

'Go on then, but don't run.'

Flash Gordon couldn't have got to the scullery quicker.

'Now, boys,' Grumps said, rolling one sleeve up above his elbow, 'this is a delicate operation.' He stared down at a barrel of Burton's bitter standing in

147

pride of place on wedges on a sturdy table in the corner of the scullery. 'First we remove the bung on top of the barrel.'

I think he was talking more to himself than to us: his concentration was intense. He produced a sack and a small shovel. Digging the shovel into the hessian bag, he produced a scoopful of fine coal dust.

'This has been washed several times,' he explained. He lifted the shovel of coal dust towards the bung hole and gently poured it into the barrel of beer. He repeated this several times with us watching every move. 'Now boys,' he said to the scullery wall, 'give the barrel a good shake.'

We set to with eager hands, but we couldn't move it; that barrel refused to budge.

Grumps laughed. 'Good try, boys.'

His laughter made us smile too. With a wooden mallet he knocked two wedges from one side of the barrel. Holding it steady with one hand, he held the mallet out for one of us to take. We both lunged at the same time.

'Don't fight,' he said gruffly. 'This barrel weighs a ton. Any tomfoolery around it will have me to answer to. Now take the hammer and be still.'

Taking hold of the barrel, the muscles in his arms bulging, he began to rock it from side to side. His tattoos began to dance on his arms. When he was satisfied, he held out his hand for the mallet – a surgeon performing a delicate operation. Bob placed it into his proffered hand.

'Right,' grunted Grumps, 'put the two wedges under the barrel, one each. Good boys, good boys.'

He banged the wooden wedges back into place, then stepped back, beads of sweat on his brow. 'Well done, well done,' he said to himself. 'Now then, where'd your mother put that piece of steak?'

148

Foraging through the larder got him nowhere. Scratching his head, he crossed the scullery to the milk-cooling cabinet. Lifting the mesh-covered lid he found what he was looking for. 'There we are!' he said in triumph. 'Right, boys, one of you pass me that carving knife on the sideboard.'

We both reached for it, but it was my turn – Bob had got the mallet. With careful precision, I put it into Grumps' outstretched hand. Knife now at the ready, he placed the steak on the marble kitchen top, spread it with his fingers and began to slice the meat into long thin pieces. 'Now boys, watch me.' He delicately placed each thin piece of steak into the barrel's bung hole. 'By the time Christmas comes those bits of steak will have fermented in there good and proper.' (The beer got steak, but we never did!) Rubbing his hands he picked up the wooden mallet, replaced the bung into its allotted hole and with one quick bang wedged it firmly into place.

'What happens now, Grumps?' I asked.

'Well now,' he said thoughtfully, 'over the next few days the coal dust will settle to the bottom, taking all the cloudy bits with it. It acts as a sort of filter, makes it all lovely and clear, like. The meat ferments on the bottom, turning sort of white, like, giving the beer a lovely juicy flavour. Lovely.' He smacked his lips in anticipation, ruffling our hair. 'You boys go out and play now.'

He smiled down on us. We looked back into his scraggly old face. To us he was not only a dad and granddad but a hero and a god.

Bob and I sauntered into the garden. Winter was coming on with a vengeance. Trees, fences and chicken coops were dusted with frozen white powder. Three-pronged footprints covered the frosty surface as the chickens pecked at the frozen ground. The feral cats were huddled together, piled on top of each other for warmth, and the rabbits' ears were twitching, their noses sniffing the cold air, while I wondered which one would be next for the stew pot.

We ambled around the garden, beginning to push each other, the pushes getting harder and harder until Bob fell over and scraped his knees. He cried out in pain but quickly got to his feet, face flushed and temper flaring. Here we go again, I thought as he charged straight at me. I managed to get him in a headlock, but this didn't stop him: fists flailing, he hit my back.

'I'll get you, I'll get you,' he said through clenched teeth.

We swung round the garden like a pair of demented dancers. If only I could pull his head off, just like Dad did to that chicken the other day, I thought. With Bob still hitting me on the back and me holding on for dear life, we continued to pirouette, churning up the mud and slush until Nan parted the kitchen curtains and banged on the window pane.

'Stop that this instant!' she screamed. 'Come in here before I box your ears!'

The menace in her voice was enough to bring us back to our senses. We parted quickly and bent double, hands on our hips, clouds of steamy breath billowing from our mouths.

'Get you next time,' threatened Bob.

'Yeh, well, we'll see,' I threatened right back.

'Come inside now and take your muddy boots off,' called Nan still staring at us through the window.

The only ones to gain were the chickens, happily pecking through the mud and slush we had left in our wake. As we re-entered the scullery, Grumps was rubbing down his barrel with a piece of rag as lovingly as if it were a prize dog.

'Grumps?'

'What, boy?' He turned towards us.

'Can we have some of that at Christmas?'

He winked, tapping his nose with his finger.

Cat-napping

'Christmas coming again soon,' said Grumps to no one in particular. 'I think we'll have to organise another race meeting.' He stroked his chin thoughtfully, his eyes mentally moving things around the garden, making room for the proposed race meeting. 'Bob! Eric!' he shouted, as he stood, hands on hips.

Chickens scurried and pecked around his feet, rabbits gnawed on carrots poked through the wire of their hutches, their big eyes watching everything; the other cages stared back emptily at him. We ran through the kitchen door and past the privy.

'Yes, Grumps?'

'I think its time for a race meeting,' he repeated.

Our hero! We both jumped up and down with excitement. 'Can we start now?'

'Well,' he said, 'let's work out how many we're going to need.' He grinned, cuffing our ears affectionately. 'How many races did we have last time, boys?'

'Six,' said Bob.

'Well, this is Christmas. Let's have ten for good measure. That's forty to catch. Start collecting tonight. You've got a week – should be time enough. Any left over, we'll skin them and sell them as rabbits again. Put some straw in the empty cages.'

We knew what to do. After preparing the empty hutches, we went to the tool shed behind the privy, getting our hunting equipment ready: rabbit snares, long forked poles, leather gloves right up to our elbows. Off we went to the bomb site just across the road. Nan was always complaining about the dust blowing in from it. Grumps always replied, 'Lucky we didn't live that side of the road.' It never failed to shut her up.

We dangled strips of whiting from snares, and placed other bits on rocks near bushes, and then lay in wait with our pronged poles. This was the worst bit – waiting silently, trying not to fidget. I wondered why I always developed itches on my face or up my bum – something to do with nerves I suppose.

As dusk descended we heard the first sounds of mewing. I nudged Bob's arm. Two cats, spitting at each other, circled the strips of whiting. Then high pitched screams tore through the night air. We pounced at the same time. I missed mine; Bob caught his with his cleft stick. The feral cat, black as midnight, screeched as it tried to turn and attack the stick that was pinning it to the rocky surface. All claws and teeth, it spat in fury, its yellow eyes flashing like deadly quicksilver.

'Quick, Eric.' Bob looked up worried.

The cat was strangling itself trying to escape. I put on my leather gloves and covered its spitting face with one hand; its fangs tore at the glove. Forcing the hessian sack over it, we managed to bundle the squirming creature into the bag, remove the stick and tie the top. Breathing heavily, we leaned on each other.

'One down, only thirty nine to go,' I said.

'And one for luck,' replied Bob.

Six cats later our front door opened and Nan

called across the street. 'Come on boys, nearly nine o'clock. Time for bed.'

'Aw Nan, five minutes more, please.'

'Please, Mum,' cried out Bob into the darkness.

'All right then, five minutes. Don't be late or I'll send Grumps over.'

We knew there would be no more hunting that night. The cats knew we were there. The hunt would get more and more difficult as the days and nights went by and they sensed we were after them. The stars came and went between the clouds; the full moon cast shadows across the bomb site; things began to move in the dark. We were sitting where old Mrs Black's fireplace used to be. She was killed when the bomb hit. Now her ghost crept through the stillness making me shudder. There were no traffic noises then, only the occasional distant hoot of a train or the sound of dogs on their nightly prowl, checking with other dogs in the area that all was well, while the pub singalong wafted down the street. The cold began to creep into our bones as the exhilaration of the night's work wore off.

'Come on, Bob, let's go.'

'What?' said Bob. 'What's up?' He had fallen asleep sitting up.

'Let's go back.'

As we made our way home, we knew there would be cocoa or Horlicks to warm us up.

Feeling through the brass letter box, my fingers closed around the piece of hemp string tied to the front door key. I opened the door and we walked down the hall passage to the back room, the sound of our footfall rising up the wooden stairwell. Nan sat next to the fire with a milk stout – dark liquid with at least two inches of creamy foam on top – Grumps with his bottle of strong barley wine. He looked up, a slight reddish glaze in his eyes.

'How many did you get boys?'

'Six, Grumps.'

'Well done, well done.'

We puffed out our chests with pride.

'Put them in the cages, then off you go to bed. Take your Horlicks with you.'

'Grumps, we've left the sacks in the passage way.'

'Good boys, I'll see to them. Off you go now.'

Clutching our Horlicks we mounted the stairs, trying not to spill the hot drinks.

'Don't make a noise when you go up; the girls are already asleep,' whispered Nan after us.

Mum and Dad were down the pub, part of the singsong we'd heard earlier. We sat together in the bedroom next to the dying embers of the fire, quietly going over the night's adventures.

'That ginger one nearly got you, Eric.'

'Yeh,' I said excitedly, 'the little bugger. But we managed to squeeze it into the sack. I could feel its claws right through the glove.'

We both sat lost in our own thoughts, our shadows thrown by the fire across the white distempered ceiling, the girls huddled together for warmth in the middle of the bed. They looked like a bundle tied up in blankets and sheets ready for Christmas posting. I felt my eyelids becoming heavy.

'Time for my bed,' I said to Bob, stretching and rubbing my eyes. I stood up, undressed absentmindedly and put on my pyjamas. As I slithered into bed, I felt Bob get in on the other side of the girls. There was no fidgeting, just calm before instant dreamless sleep. We never felt or heard Nan come in to make sure all was well.

The next day Bob and I set off again. 'Let's go

further afield. There are so many bomb sites around, and they'll be expecting us at our one.'

'Good idea,' said Bob. 'We can take my bike; we'll be able to tie the sacks to the back.'

And so Christmas and the cat races crept towards us.

Grumps' Delivery

'Right, boys, the lorry will be arriving in about an hour, so don't go away. I need you to unload the crates with the delivery men.'

'OK, Grumps,' I said.

'Make sure there's nothing on the stairs and landings. We'll have to be sharp about it when the lorry gets here.'

It was just before Christmas. Grumps explained that this delivery was his and Uncle Jack's Christmas present for working so hard in the brewery all year.

'Why are you winking at Uncle Jack, Grumps?' I asked, all innocence.

'Nothing son, just got something in my eye.'

Still we believed him. (We believed him right up until the day he died. Our childish naiveté makes me smile even today.) Bob and I rushed into the hall to clear away the brooms that were behind the front door, the adults and kiddies boots that were scattered on the stairs and landing, and the coats hanging from the banister rail. The coming Christmas added excitement and we could hear our mums laughing to each other in the kitchen as we made our way upstairs, looking for any other offending object. We looked out of the front bedroom window when a muffled voice was heard.

'Here it comes,' said my dad, down at street level.

Bob and I craned our necks to look along the empty street. Sure enough, we could just see the Tollymache lorry turning into our road. We ran down the stairs two at a time. The lorry roared towards us, its diesel fumes making us all cough. Beer bottles clinked in their crates as it came to a screeching halt and two men jumped out even before it had fully stopped. You could hear the driver ratcheting the handbrake on, and then he followed the other two men to the rear where large lettering in green and gold proudly announced to the public: 'TOLLEMACHE'S – THE OLDEST BREWERY IN THE EAST END'.

'Look lively!' said the driver.

'Put 'em all in the front garden; we'll do the rest.'

Two draymen jumped up onto the lorry, tailboarding off the wooden crates of clinking bottles full of frothing beer: milk stout, brown ale, light ale and best bitter. In their haste to unload, several bottle tops exploded, sending froth cascading down their leather aprons and onto their boots.

'Look out boys, or there'll be nothing left for Christmas.'

They all laughed, breaking the tension of knowing they would get the chop if they were ever caught. We formed a chain to the front garden. As we passed them from one to the other, the crates began to stack up. Everyone began to grunt with the effort as sweat poured off us all. Half an hour later, the lorry empty, we all leaned on the garden wall trying to get our breath back.

'Right,' said Grumps, breathing heavily. 'That's the lot then. See you three at the party on Boxing Day.'

All three draymen nodded their acknowledgement, still breathing too heavily to speak. They climbed back into the lorry's cab and the engine sparked into life; they drove away in another ballooning cloud of diesel smoke.

Each crate had **Tollemache** burnt on its side.

'Get that tarpaulin over the crates; we don't want the neighbours nicking any.'

The irony of Grumps' comment went over our heads, but we knew that none of the neighbours would dare touch the crates with Grumps around.

'Take a beer each and rest for a bit,' he added. 'You boys get yourselves a lemonade. The worst is yet to come.'

Uncle Jack nodded his head knowingly. Bob and I gulped our lemonade in the kitchen, listening to the men grunting and humping the crates into the house and up the stairs past the first landing. Placing our glasses on the wooden draining board next to the butler sink, we rushed back to the hallway.

'Can we help?'

'Go and help your uncle in the front garden.'

Gradually the pile of crates found its way up the next set of stairs onto the top landing. They stacked the crates one by one, starting at the end nearest the banisters, floor to ceiling around the walls, leaving openings for the two bedrooms; then down the first set of stairs onto the next landing, up the walls, again leaving a gap for the third bedroom, around that landing and down the main staircase to the bottom passage; along the bottom passage, floor to ceiling went the Tollemache crates, the last few squeezed in behind the front door. The front door now only opened halfway, meaning you had to shuffle sideways to get in or out. This would not please Nan as she was somewhat on the larger than life size. Still,

Christmas was Christmas and our parties were larger than life, too. A family party would involve the whole street and maybe several streets beyond – everybody welcome, a wink and a blink regarding the beer.

'It always tastes better when it's free,' Grumps remarked to no one in particular.

After Christmas, all the empty bottles and crates were stacked against the outside back wall, almost reaching to the second floor window. Bob and I knew what to do to destroy the evidence, but at the time we didn't know why we were doing it. Fetching our spades and forks from the garden shed we dug a trench two foot wide and four foot deep – the same every year. We then put the empty beer bottles into the trench, got long iron bars and began to crush the bottles. We then added another layer of bottles and repeated the process until all the wooden crates were empty. With the trench now three-quarters full of crushed glass, we filled the hole with as much of the earth as possible. The rest went into the wheelbarrow and across the road to be dumped on the bomb site. When we walked on the bottom half of the garden, we could hear the broken bottles crunching underfoot. Next, Bob and I broke up the crates with axes, stacking the pieces along the back of the privy.

'Should keep the fires burning for some time,' remarked Bob. We stood there plucking the splinters out of our hands. But it was worth it.

Will-'o-the-wisp

'Cor, luv a duck, Albert, you're not going to pull that old chestnut from the fire again. We've been down that road three times already.'

'Nah, they won't remember. It was last year.'

'Yeah, and the year before that, and the one before that, and so on,' said my dad.

'We'll get the boys in on this one.' Grumps sat poking the fire. Sparks spat back at him and a hot coal fell from the fire onto the tiled hearth.

'Be careful, Albert. We don't want the floorboards alight,' Nan warned from behind the two men.

'Stop nagging, Rose. I'll be careful.' Concentration on his thoughts was in his eyes. 'We'll get the boys to take the raffle tickets to school ... get the teachers to buy some ... they won't know.'

I knelt next to Grumps, warming my outstretched hands, and looked over at Bob kneeling the other side of the hearth. He shrugged his shoulders and his eyes rolled skywards as if to say, we'll find out in due course. We'd seen so many scams from Grumps and my dad, we knew it wouldn't be long before we were told what was going on.

'Yeah,' Grumps mumbled to himself, 'the boys can help. They're old enough now. Have to go to a few pubs further afield ... can't pull this one too close to home. How much are those books of raffle tickets, Charlie?'

163

'A shilling each,' Dad replied.

'Right.' Grumps fumbled in his waistcoat pocket. Three shiny shilling pieces jingled in his outstretched palm. 'Boys, go to the offy, get three books of raffle tickets – different colours, mind.'

We scrambled to our feet.

'Here's a ha'penny each. Get yourselves a gobstopper.'

Pushing each other, we ran out of the door.

'Wipe your feet on the way back in and don't slam the door!' shouted Nan.

'Yes Nan!' Our voices rang down the hall. We never could see what all the fuss was about. There were bare floorboards in the hall and on the stairs, a square of lino in the parlour, the surrounding floorboards painted black with the paint finishing just under the lino, and the scullery and kitchen floors were concrete. Nothing there that couldn't cope with a bit of dirt.

'I'm sure that bleedin' door's going to fall off its hinges the way those boys shut it,' said Nan to nobody in particular. No one listened, and she knew it. 'Bloody kids,' she said as she shuffled back into the kitchen. We slammed the door behind us in defiance.

'Have we got time for our weekly pocket money?' I asked as we reached the off licence.

'I think Dad can spare us for a few moments.' Bob winked at me. 'Have a doggo round the corner, El. Make sure no one's coming.'

I looked up and down the road. 'All clear, Bob. Whose turn to shin up the lamppost? Don't matter, I'll do it.'

We were at the back of the off licence, squeezed into a small back alleyway, the street light still on, shining down like a belisha beacon.

'Up you go, Eric, I'll help you.'

He stood by the side of the lamppost, hands cupped ready for my foot. With one heave, I launched myself upward. The concrete post swayed slightly, the rough surface scuffing the inside of my bare legs. Wriggling like a worm, I scuttled to the top. Hanging on with both legs and one arm, I could just reach over the barbed wire at the top of the fence.

'Can you reach any, El?' Bob whispered up to me.

I looked down and nodded. With every sinew stretched to its limits, my fingertips wrapped around the first one. 'Make sure you catch it, Bob.'

He held up his hands. 'Shut up, you know I'm the best wicket keeper in the school.'

After dropping eight, I began to shin down the post, scratching the inside of my thighs again. Short trousers were not very good for these occasions.

'You didn't take them from the same crate, did you El?'

'Don't be silly, I'm not that daft.' We both laughed. The insides of my legs stung and the grazes were seeping little droplets of blood. 'I bagsy the extra 4d for me wounds, Bob.'

'I bagsy we split it fifty-fifty. Look at the palms of my hands.' Blood seeped from deep scratches. 'That's your mum's studded shoes for you.'

A bell tinkled as we opened the door and entered the shop. "Morning, Mr. Brooks. Can we have three books of raffle tickets, please – different colours?'

"Morning, boys.' He ran his fingers over the lemonade bottles, counting. 'Eight,' he said to himself. 'That's one shilling and fourpence. Where you boys getting these bottles from, eh?'

'Bomb sites, dustbins, street gutters,' we replied innocently.

'That's a lot of money for you two.'

'Yes, we know, but if people are too lazy to collect the deposits, we'll do it for 'em.'

He laughed, scratching his head. 'That will be three shillings, less the deposit money.'

'Oh can we have that separate please?' Bob plonked three shillings and two halfpennies on the counter top. 'And two gobstoppers.'

'Very well.'

After handing over our purchases, he opened the till drawer and put a shiny silver shilling and four copper pennies on the counter.

'Cor look, Bob. There's two pennies with Queen Victoria on 'em. Thanks Mr Brooks. We'll see you soon. Our dads are waiting for us.'

We ran out of the offy door heading for home, raffle tickets tucked safely in our pockets. Other boys from school, out playing in the street, tried to trip us up as we passed. 'We'll get you at school, Charlie Green; you too, Billy Brown. You wait!' All this as we leapt over their outstretched legs.

Bully boy Biggins came out of his front door. He was the same age as us but bigger. He saw us running down our street and stood in front of us, waiting for us to run past him so that he could cuff us round our ears. Bob and I exchanged glances. Heads down, we increased our speed. *Crash!* Biggins didn't have time to get out of the way. Our heads slammed into his chest, knocking all the breath from his body. He went down, cracking his head on the pavement. Bob kicked his left kneecap; I kicked his right. A cry of pain left his lips.

'Sorry Harry, didn't see you standing there. Can't stop, our dads are waiting for us.' We ran on.

'I'll get you at school! You wait and see!' he cried as he sat there rubbing his knees, tears running down his cheeks. 'I'll get you! Just you wait and see!'

We laughed to ourselves. We knew he wouldn't.

'Wipe your feet,' Nan called from the kitchen when we opened the front door. She always had eyes in the back of her head.

'Yes Nan.'

'Cor, Eric, put the wood in the hole, will you? It's freezing out there.'

'Yes Dad.'

'Come in here boys; let's see what you've got. Right Charlie, you go out towards Whipps Cross ... several pubs out that way. You know anyone out there?'

'Only on nodding terms.'

'You take the blue raffle book, I'll take the yellow one. I'll head up Shernhall Street ... couple of pubs up there ... then down the high street ... same as you Charlie, a few men on nodding terms, nothing special. You boys ... school on Monday ... ask the headmaster. What's his name?'

'Mr Maxwell.'

'Well ask him if we can raffle the bird. Tell him we'll donate ten bob towards the school funds. That should do it. Charlie, no good going today ... missed the dinner opening times. Start tomorrow. Rose!' Grumps shouted at the kitchen door.

'What now?' came the caustic reply.

'Charlie and me will be out all day tomorrow, so don't worry about grub; we'll take care of ourselves ... eat on the hoof as it were.'

'What about the boys?' asked Nan through the kitchen wall.

'Same as usual,' barked Grumps.

Tomorrow came too quickly. I didn't like the thought of approaching Mr Maxwell. We did not get

167

on at the best of times. Any trouble in my year, I somehow had to be one of the culprits. It never mattered to him whether I was guilty or innocent: I was always guilty as charged. 'Line up outside Mr Maxwell's office,' commanded one teacher or another, even if I hadn't been in the school when whatever incident had happened. Guilty by association.

This time, standing outside the headmaster's office felt quite strange.

'Come in.'

My hand trembled as I turned the round brass handle.

'You again, Bartholomew? What trouble have you been in this time?'

'None, sir. I've come to ask your permission to raffle a chicken. My Grumps and my dad said if all the raffle tickets sold in the school they would give a donation.'

'Hmm. What's it all about?'

'Er … m-my Grumps breeds chickens in the back garden. (I wish I was there now, I thought to myself.)

'Well, go on, boy, go on.'

'Sorry sir. Every year, Grumps and Dad raffle the fattest one. Most of the money goes to charity.'

'Very commendable. How do we know who wins?' enquired the head.

He leaned forward, his beady eyes looking right through me. I took a mental picture of the punishment canes hanging on the wall.

'The winning numbers are posted at the post office and the off licence on the weekend before Christmas, sir. Chicken to be delivered on Christmas Eve.' I stood my ground. I wanted to pee and shit myself at the same time, but managed not to show any fear.

'Very well, Bartholomew, you have my permission to go to the teachers' staff room and sell as many tickets as you can. By the way, how much are they?'

My bum relaxed. 'Five tickets for a shilling, sir.'

'Very well.'

He reached inside his waistcoat pocket and held out a shilling piece. I scrambled through my pocket, holding out the guilty raffle tickets. Mr Maxwell picked his tickets at random and wrote his name on the stubs.

'How d'you get on, Eric?' Dad asked as I came through the front door. I didn't even have time to take off my school cap or put down my satchel.

'Sold the lot, Dad. But I got asked lots of questions.'

'Well done, lad.' He ruffled my hair.

Bob barged through the open door, nearly knocking me sideways. 'Dad, Uncle Charlie, I've sold the lot!'

'Where d'you sell 'em?' barked Grumps.

'Most of them went to the mums and dads picking up their kids.'

'Good boys! Good boys!' There were smiles all round. 'Let's pool the money on the table and have a count up.' The sound of tinkling shillings was music to our ears. 'That's not a bad profit for a chicken that doesn't exist,' laughed Grumps.

'I don't like it. Albert, Charlie, you mark my words: it's all right with a few bar flies, but involving the boys' school ... well, that's another matter.'

'Aw, Rose, you're always such a pessimist.'

Nan shuffled back to the kitchen, muttering to herself again.

The weekend before Christmas crept round. The winner's name and number were duly posted at the off licence and the post office. Two days later, on Christmas Eve, a loud knock echoed round the hallway. Nan went to open the door. The hallway stayed dark as the bulky frame of Constable Parkin filled the doorway.

'Is Albert or Charlie in, Mrs Rose?'

'Albert, you're wanted!' was all Nan said – at the top of her voice.

'Who is it?' came a muffled cry from the back garden.

'Excuse me, Constable.' Nan moved back down the gloomy hallway.

Grumps' head appeared around the back room door. 'What's up, Constable?'

'Seems one of the school teachers has complained about the raffle, Albert.'

'What complaint?' asked Grumps.

'Seems like this teacher checked up on the winner, who, according to your postings, lives at 96 Chester Road. Seems there's no such number. The road finishes at 94.'

'What?' said Grumps. 'Must be some mistake.'

'That's what I'm hoping you or Charlie can clear up for us. This teacher's not going to let this rest, Albert.'

'Constable, can you give me a couple of hours till Charlie comes home? Must be some mistake.' Grumps was clearly rattled.

'That's what they thought down at the station.' He looked at Albert with a knowing eye. 'I'll be back in a couple of hours. This is very serious, Albert. See you soon.'

Constable Parkin walked away and light shone back into the hallway.

'I told you no good would come of this!' screamed Nan after closing the front door.

'I know all that,' said Grumps, going white. 'But that ain't going to get us out of this mess.'

Bob and I kept quiet. Running through my mind was what might happen at school.

Some time later my dad walked through the front door. 'I'm home.'

'Charlie!' barked Grumps, 'Come out here!'

Dad disappeared out into the back yard. Bob and I heard muffled arguing with the occasional squawk from Nan. We knew something was in the air. We heard a chicken squeal its loud death throes in the yard. Then the three of them came back into the kitchen together, Grumps carrying the dead chicken.

'Rose, get the pot on for boiling water. Where's my gutting knife? You boys stay where you are.'

No explanation was given while we waited.

'Rose, is that water boiled yet?'

'Just coming, Albert. Just a mo'.'

Bob and I exchanged glances and watched the proceedings. The smell of dead chicken got stronger and the plucked and gutted bird was finally hanging upside down from Grumps' hand.

'Get the greaseproof paper and wrap the bird, Rose. You boys take it round to 69 Chester Road. Tell them: "Congratulations, you won the raffle".'

We left with the smelly bird still warm, ran all the way to Chester Road and knocked on the door of number 69. A short man with a bald head and a large beard opened the door. I wondered why bald men always tried to grow upside down hair.

'Congratulations, our dads sent us round with the winning chicken for you.'

'What winning chicken?'

I explained about the Christmas raffle. 'First

prize, this chicken.' I held it up in front of me.

'What raffle? I didn't do no raffle?'

A large lady, a foot taller than her husband, a scarf over her wire curlers, came up behind him and looked down on us with hard eyes. 'What's this?'

'This pair said we won a chicken in some raffle. I ain't done no raffle.'

I saw her elbow crack into his ear. 'Well maybe one of your mates down at the local bought you some tickets.' She reached over his head, snatched the bird from our grasp and slammed the door in our faces. From the other side of the door I could hear, 'You bleedin' idiot! When was the last time we could afford chicken? 'Course you bought tickets!'

We ran home laughing. That had been a close one. Our dads would be pleased with us.

A loud bang heralded Constable Parkin's return. I let him in. The sound of carol singers up and down the streets came in the open front door, and the smell of roasting potatoes wafted out as hanging paper chains in the hallway rustled in the draught. I saw a drunken man weaving his way home, a silly coloured paper hat set jauntily on the side of his head.

Grumps was ready with his explanation. 'Our mistake, Constable: I thought the number was 96 but Charlie informed me it was 69. I wrote it down wrong. My mistake.'

'Has the bird been delivered?'

'Yes, Constable Parkin.'

'Very well, I'll inform my officer and we'll relay this information to the school after the holidays. You shouldn't hear any more about it. But if it happens again ... well, that would be silly, wouldn't it?'

'Yes Constable, that would be daft.'

'Well goodnight then. Merry Christmas.'

172

As he turned to see himself out, I saw him smile to himself. 'Cheeky buggers,' he murmured, shaking his head. A wry laugh left him as the front door slammed behind him and he pounded his way down the street.

The Fight

Christmas came and went after too much drinking, too much dinner and too much Christmas pud. Grumps had drunk his beer and rubbed his chest, complaining about indigestion as he burped his way through his bicarbonate of soda. Uncle Jack had got pissed on the first day and been ill for the rest of the holiday. The cat races had gone well. Nan nagged, Mum's and Aunt Vera's hands went white and wrinkly from all the washing up, and everyone flopped around in their new slippers. This year, Bob, June and I had been lucky: we got three main presents each.

A few days after Christmas, Bob and I came rushing into the back room from the bomb site. We couldn't play outside for very long on those dark and freezing January days.

'Have you boys wiped your feet?' Nan yelled.

'Yes, Nan,' we chorused automatically.

Grumps was sitting with a bowl on his lap and his hands immersed in a brackish substance.

'What's that, Dad?' asked Bob.

'Walnut juice and vinegar,' he replied. 'Toughens yer 'ands up.'

'What do you want to do that for, Grumps?'

'You'll see, you'll see. All in good time. Now, help your Nan to lay the table. Supper's ready.'

'Piccalilli sandwiches and strawberry jam with marge on toast.' There was an apologetic note in her voice.

I did as I was told and sat at the table waiting for the meal. I could hear Mum's and Nan's voices in the kitchen.

'The money's all gone over Christmas. We'll have to pull our belts in for a few weeks.'

'Don't worry, Mum, we'll get by somehow.'

Grumps just sat there broodily, his hands still immersed in the brackish water.

For the next two weeks, every time Bob and I came home, Grumps was sitting staring into the fire with his hands in a bowl.

A Saturday night arrived.

'Come on Eric, you're coming with me.'

'Can I come too, Dad? Please?' Bob hated to be left out.

'Not tonight. Your mother will explain.'

Bob began to cry and Grumps reached over and whacked him hard about his head.

'Grow up, boy. Stop snivelling. Crying's for girls. Be a man now.'

He marched out of the room with me in tow, almost running to try and keep up with him. Out into the cold, dark, winter's night, down the road, past the school we went. The school gates were closed. The tall Victorian building, silhouetted against the sky, looked menacing and, to my young eyes, haunted. We turned the corner into Wood Street, our local shopping street, and stopped outside a pub called The Flower Pot.

'Now, you wait 'ere,' instructed Grumps. 'I won't be long.'

He opened the door to the public bar. Warmth enveloped me and the lights from inside dazzled me; I put my hands in front of my eyes to shield them. The noise from the men inside was deafening and with the door fully open all the pipe, cigarette and cigar smoke tried to escape through the available space. It whirled around me, making me splutter and cough. I stepped back and the door slammed shut, cutting out the warmth and the light. The cold crept back around me and the smoke rose sedately into the air, making me feel like a cold dog end. I sat down on the stone step, rubbing my cold knees, my breath steaming onto my winter coat. When the door suddenly opened again, I half fell into the public bar.

'Get up now,' said Grumps. 'Here's an arrowroot biscuit and a glass of ginger beer.'

I hated ginger beer. I took it, wishing it was sarsaparilla or cream soda, and sat down again, remembering not to lean on the door. I waited, without any idea of what I was waiting for. Two policemen came strolling down the street, their hobnail boots clattering on the cobbles. 'Evening,' they said as they passed. They always patrolled in twos in this neighbourhood, ever since one of them had tried bully boy tactics on some of the locals and they had drowned him down a rainwater manhole. They put his hat next to the manhole and left his feet just above the hole. That's what I was told, anyhow.

I thought I'd take a peek inside the pub to see what Grumps was doing. Pushing the door slightly open, I saw him standing by the bar. My eyes began to water as the beer and tobacco fumes came to meet me and I put my hand over my mouth, trying to stifle a cough. Grumps was looking around. He knew most of the people there and they knew him.

'Right!' he shouted above the din, slamming his fist on the bar counter. 'Who wants to have a rout?'

The bar went quiet. Most of the men knew Grumps of old.

'No one for a knuckle?' He looked around menacingly.

177

'How much then?' The question came from a man sitting on a stool.

'Half a crown a go, the winner takes all, the loser gets a pint of Guinness to rub on his sores.'

The pub erupted into laughter. These men were the salt of the earth, hard men, survivors from the Great War, some of their sons killed in the second. They had all stared death in the eye many times; none of them was averse to a fight. But not with Albert. They had all seen what he could do to a man.

'Any takers?' growled Grumps.

Silence rained down; some of the men sipped their beer, some carried on smoking. Grumps looked at a table of strangers sitting in a corner drinking their mugs of frothy beer.

'Any of you care to take me on?'

One of them looked Grumps straight in the eye. 'How do?' said the stranger. 'I'm from Bethnal Green. How much did you say?'

'Two and six and all the side bets are yours.'

'I'll give it a go.'

His hard eyes never left Grumps as he stood up. People began to mutter, everyone glancing at the stranger. He stood at least a foot taller than Grumps and was a lot thicker set. He took off his coat and walked towards the bar, his eyes still fixed on Grumps, who stared back.

The landlord stepped up. 'You both set on this then?'

They stared at each other, nodding their consent.

'Right, then, these are the rules: no kicking, no gouging, no biting. Other than that, don't kill each other. Strip to the waist and I'll take the bets.'

The two fighting men placed their respective half crowns on the bar counter, and their eyes locked as they stripped. The stranger looked very fit: not an ounce of fat anywhere and muscles that bulged alarmingly. Grumps looked slight up against him.

'Place your bets, gentlemen,' instructed the landlord.

Everyone left their tables at the same time, digging into their pockets, change jangling in their upturned hands. The betting stacked up, favouring the stranger despite Grumps' reputation. He looked like David against Goliath – without the slingshot.

'Who's going to hold the purse?' inquired the landlord.

'The boy will,' said Grumps.

'What boy?' the stranger asked.

I quickly closed the heavy door, turned around and sat on the step, ready to feign surprise. Bare-chested, Grumps swung open the pub door and dragged me in by my shirt collar. The warmth was welcoming. Everybody stared at me and I recognised some of the men as Grumps lifted me up and plonked me on the bar top.

'Now Eric, see this stranger here?'

I nodded my head.

'Well, me and him are going out the back for a little chat, see, and you'll hand the purse to whoever walks back through the door first. You got it, lad?' He placed a hand on my shoulder and gave it a gentle squeeze.

'Seems fair to me,' said the stranger.

'Why you got no clothes on top, Grumps?'

'Because it's so bleedin' 'ot in 'ere, innit?'

He walked out of the back door, followed by the stranger and the whole pub crowd. Only the landlord and his wife remained, counting the two piles of coins and putting them all in the purse, which they handed to me.

'There's ten guineas in there, boy. I think your granddad's bitten off more than he can handle this time. You make sure you do as he says now: you hand the bag to whichever man walks through the door.'

I sat on the counter, bemused, the heavy purse dangling between my hands. All I could hear through the back door were grunts, curses and comments from the crowd. 'Go on, hit him again!' 'Kill the bastard!' I jumped off the bar. The heavy purse jangled as I hit the floor and looked up at the landlord and his wife.

'You want to see what's going on?'

'Don't you think he's a bit young?' said his wife.

'He might as well learn now as any other time,' retorted the landlord. 'Don't go outside the door; you might get trampled on.'

I turned towards the noise. Opening the back door, I saw my Grumps and the stranger toe to toe, fists raised high. The stranger hit my Grumps. I cried out in anguish, my eyes wide, my mouth open. No one heard me; they were all intent on what was in front of them, their baying blood lust a palpable thing in the air. The stranger had hit Grumps hard on the shoulder. Spinning him round and catching him off guard as he tried to regain his balance, he then clubbed Grumps with his right fist, bringing it down on the side of his head. Grumps went down like a poleaxed bear as the grinning stranger straightened from his crouched position. The baying crowd fell silent, half of them undoubtedly wondering if that was all they were going to get for their money, the other half already mentally counting their winnings.

The creature on the muddy ground stirred, no longer my Grumps but a raging animal, blood running from his right ear. He stood straight, then

180

stooped in the manner of a fighter, fists clenched. I no longer recognised my Grumps.

'Is that the best you've got?' he spat at his enemy, spattering mucous on the man's boots.

The smile left the stranger's face and he crouched once more. The bar flies could feel the power of Grumps' rage and they shivered with fear. They knew one of these men was not going home tonight; not far away, Whipps Cross hospital beckoned. The stranger roared and rushed at Grumps, trying to get him in a bear hug, no doubt hoping to crush the life out of him. Grumps ducked under his embrace and hit him as hard as he could on his left rib cage. There was an audible crack. The man pulled up short, his breath coming out with a whoosh; a look of pained puzzlement appeared on his face. Twenty years separated these two, youth against a crazy man who loved the nectar of pain: it made his blood rush through his veins and his primeval spirit rise to the surface.

The stranger looked into Grumps' eyes, as if to acknowledge that in his heart he knew he would lose the fight. But his anger soared, pushing him on. The men in the crowd roared in unison, releasing all their own frustration and cowardice.

'Kill 'im! Tear the bastard limb from limb!' they screamed. 'Break 'im in 'alf! Gouge 'is eyes out!'

The two fighters circled each other, the only thought in their minds to savage each other. Mud splashes covered them and courses of sweat found pathways down their bodies like camouflage. The stranger favoured his left side, keeping his arm protectively against his ribs. Grumps knew that was his target. He came on, feigned to the right, the other man followed him. His fist smacked into Grumps' nose. I heard another crack. Blood spattered everyone.

Some of it reached me and I tasted my grandfather's bittersweet blood.

Concentrating on the stranger's torso, Grumps hit him on the same spot as before and there was another audible crack of ribs breaking. They stepped back from each other, the big man holding his side. Blood ran from both of Grumps' nostrils into his mouth. I watched him suck it in and then spit it out, breathing hard as he put up his hand to feel the deep cut on the bridge of his nose. 'Two black eyes for breakfast again,' he said. I was surprised at the sideways grin on his face. Grumps must have known he could never knock this man out, but everyone sensed the stranger's reluctance to go on. The broken ribs would wake up soon and cause agonies beyond belief.

'Toe the line, sunshine! Toe the line!' shouted someone in the crowd.

Grumps spat a mixture of spittle and blood at his opponent. The man responded and put his boot to the line. Grumps did not wait. Rushing forward, he pummelled the man's hurt body, left and right, left and right, hitting his broken ribs again and again, forcing him back step by step until he was pressed against the crowd. I heard his grunts of pain, saw blows hitting Grumps' face, knocking his head from side to side. His left eye began to close as they stood toe to toe, pummelling each other. I heard another rib go, then another. My heart pounded and tears streamed down my face. As if I could take every blow for my hero, my little fists were clenched so tightly my knuckles turned white and began to throb while involuntary sobs of shock and frustration left my open mouth.

The bigger man weakened, which spurred Grumps on. He seemed to feel no pain now. Unaware of the screaming crowd, it was as if he heard only the creature in front of him crying out like a wounded animal in its death throes. My Grumps stepped back, clutching his chest and shaking his head, trying to clear his vision. He stepped forward again, lashing out blindly, and the stranger went down, sitting in the mud with his breath coming in agonised rafts. Grumps moved away, his whole head covered in mud, blood and spittle. He gulped for air, clutching his chest again. Two of the crowd threw buckets of cold water over each man. 'Toe the line!' someone shouted again.

Grumps stepped forward. The stranger stayed seated in the mud, head bowed, chin nestling into his heaving chest.

'Toe the line!'

The seated man did not move. Grumps lowered his guard and placed his hands on his knees, trying to focus his one good eye. We knew he'd won. Clutching his chest, his became himself again, returning from wherever he had been, while the stranger's friends helped the broken fighter to his feet, pain showing clearly on his face. 'You'd better get 'im to 'ospital,' someone said as his friends threw his overcoat round his shoulders and half carried him towards the back door.

'Wait a minute!' growled Grumps. 'The first one to go through that door is going to be me.'

Everyone stopped. Grumps eyed each one in turn as he walked back into the bar. I shut the door and ran past him, scrambling as best I could back up onto the counter. Scuffing my eyes dry with my coat sleeve, I tasted my own blood where I'd inadvertently bitten through my bottom lip. The agony of seeing my Grumps all battered and bruised started me crying again. I bit my lip once more, trying to fight back the tears. The heavy purse jangled mockingly as I sat there. All I saw was this bloodied creature walking towards me, his hair matted and one eye closed. His head was covered in blood, which dripped off his chin to run down his body and soak into his trousers. He took the purse from me, put on his overcoat and slung his shirt over his shoulder.

'Come on, boy,' he said, holding out his bloodied, bruised hand to me.

I jumped off the counter and followed him out into the cold night air.

'I 'ate 'em all! Parasites!' he said to nobody in particular. Then he looked down at me with his one good eye. 'Come on, son, let's go home.'

We walked down Wood Street, eyes following us all the way. Curtains moved, then settled once more into indifference. Turning from the street light into a dimly lit side street, Grumps hesitated and leaned against the darkened wall. Slowly he slid and scraped his way down to squat on his haunches.

'Dear me, that's a queer'un.' He rubbed his bare chest. 'Give me a few minutes,' he grunted, 'and I'll be all right. Go back and stand at the corner. Anyone comes, you let me know.'

Standing half in light and half in shadow, I watched for people. It was odd seeing Grumps rocking backwards and forwards; I'd never seen him do that before.

'Cor, my bleedin' 'eart,' he muttered, his face drained of all colour and energy. He stopped moving, the pain in his chest obviously excruciating. 'Come on old son, pull yourself together,' he muttered to himself. He looked at me standing just in the shadows, keeping dog eye. 'Good boy,' he said. 'How long have I been sitting here?' He could not recall. I had not moved and no one had come past. I helped pull him up the wall, placing my hand on his chest as I steadied him. The shock of feeling his heart beating out of rhythm made me step back.

'Ready, son?' He balanced himself away from the wall, took a deep breath and set off home. Colour began to seep back into his ashen face. 'Your Nan will give me hell in the morning when she sees me. Can't be helped.'

My Hero

'Dinner will be ready soon. June! Christine!' Nan bellowed through the kitchen walls. 'Come in from the garden and help set the table. You boys, come in and wash yourselves.'

We stopped playing. Her command was always final. Even the chickens stopped pecking for an instant. Bob and I tried to brush the mud off our hands and knees, only making it worse.

'Grab some grass; rub it with that,' said June.

'Good idea,' I said, grabbing great chunks of the tufted stuff and handing some to Bob. We soon looked a bit more presentable and headed for the kitchen door.

'Wipe your feet, you lot.'

'Yes Nan.'

'Blimey, Rose, my old ticker's giving me some jip.'

'Serves you right. Look at you – two black eyes, bruises everywhere. What are you doing, fighting at your age? It's about time you grew up.' Nan stood with chest thrust forward, hands on hips, her pinny bursting at the seams. 'Sit down for a minute, take the weight off your feet, Albert.'

'Give us a beer, Rose. It might clear me chest.'

'No beer for you, just rest.' Nan turned and walked back into the kitchen.

Warm smells of hot food wafted towards us:

187

steak and kidney steamed pud dancing up and down in the pan, its cotton covering tied on tight; a cauldron bubbling away with pease pudding; mounds of boiling potatoes, turned yellow by a generous dollop of English mustard; real peas bobbing up and down in hot sugary water.

'I'm starving, Mum,' said Bob, rubbing saliva from his drooling mouth onto his sleeve.

Nan cuffed him round the ear. 'How many times do I have to tell you? Stop cuffing snot onto your clothes. It makes 'em go shiny.'

'Ow, Mum, that hurt!'

'Serves you right. Now wash your hands ready for your tea. You all right in there, Albert?' Nan boomed.

A muffled reply came from the back room.

'Come on girls, get cracking! Grab those knives and forks and go and lay the table.'

June and Christine went into the back room. June immediately popped her head back into the kitchen. 'Nan, Grandad's fallen asleep on the floor.'

Nan went stiff. Wiping her hands nervously, she dashed as quick as lightning into the other room. I followed.

'Albert!' she cried out anxiously.

He lay at an awkward angle, one arm tucked under his body and his head tilted backwards. The chair was lying on its side.

'Albert! Albert!'

She knelt by his side, rubbing his other hand. We four stood there awkwardly, not knowing what to do, shifting from one foot to the other.

Grumps coughed and stirred. 'Blimey, Rose, what happened?'

'You fell off the chair,' she replied nervously.

'Don't remember a thing. It was like someone

switching off the light.' He tried to sit up, but with one arm pinned beneath his body, his efforts failed.

'Lie still for a minute,' soothed Nan as she turned to us. 'One of you girls go and get a drink of water. Boys, help me get him up.'

All three of us eased him off the floor. Nan righted the chair.

'Sit down for a bit.'

'Don't mind if I do.'

His face was ashen as he wobbled on his feet. Nan placed the chair behind him and he sat down heavily.

'Cor that's a turn up for the books.' Some colour crept back into his cheeks.

'I'll go and get the doctor.'

'No you won't, Rose! No need for that. Just let me rest here for a while. Must have overdone it a bit last night.'

'Overdone it a bit, you soppy old sod? No more fighting for you from now on, you silly old git.' Tears ran down her cheeks and she dabbed at them with the dishcloth. 'Now look what you've done – got me all upset.' She wiped her eyes again.

'Now don't you fret, Rose, I'll be all right in a minute.'

My dad walked in from the front door, bringing the cold and damp with him. He stood by the open fire rubbing his hands. 'Blimey, it's cold out there.' He looked around, sensing that something was wrong. 'What's up?'

'Albert blacked out just before you came in.'

'I'm all right, Rose. Stop fussing.'

'Nan,' June piped up, 'I think there's something burning in the kitchen.

'Blimey!' She rushed back into the kitchen. 'The spuds are burning!'

189

We all heard the crash as she threw the cauldron of spuds into the butler sink. 'Ruined!'

'You all right Albert?' enquired Dad, concern in his voice.

'I'm all right. Pass me a beer, Charlie. You boys, go and see if your Nan needs a hand. You girls, set the table.'

We pretended not to hear. Dad handed Grumps a quart bottle of beer. He popped the top off, lifted the neck of the bottle to his lips, tossed his head back and pulled on the beer, his great Adam's apple working overtime. His head came forward and he smacked his lips, wiping foam from around his mouth.

'Aaaah that's better!' A great burp left his mouth. 'That's what it was, trapped wind. I feel better already.'

Two voices could be heard laughing as the front door opened and slammed shut once more. Mum and Aunt Vera came in, shopping bags in each hand and their hair in curlers, held in place by the usual brightly coloured scarves. The smell of dampness and cold reached our nostrils.

'Come in and shut the door. You've brought the cold in with you,' growled Grumps, resting his beer bottle on his knee.

'Keep your hair on, Dad. We've been down the Co-op. Got all this with my "divi".'

Mum held out one heavy bag, expecting Grumps to examine its contents. He ignored her, taking another pull on his beer.

'I think your mother's burnt the dinner. You'd better go and have a look-see.'

Aunt Vera and Mum looked at each other, and then rushed towards the kitchen, bags still held firmly as they disappeared into the steam-filled room.

'I told you boys to go and help as well.'

We reluctantly followed. Nan stood over the butler sink, saving as many of the potatoes as she could. Tears rolled down her cheeks, ran off her chin and hissed as they splashed onto the scalding pan. Mum and Aunt Vera dropped their bags and rushed over to her, reaching out to touch her tenderly on the shoulder.

'What's up, Mum?'

'Don't want no more heartache ... my eldest boy killed in that bloody war ... don't want no more grief in this 'ouse.' She seemed not to notice they were there, as if she was talking to herself. 'Albert's just blacked out ... getting too old to fight like that, silly old bugger ... don't want no more heartache, see?' Her mighty frame shook as great streams of tears ran down her face.

Both sisters embraced her, tears welling up in their eyes. 'It'll be all right, you'll see.' They hugged her to them,

'Remember your brother Albert, how he waved goodbye, so happy go lucky like? He was so proud in his naval uniform, the way his cap sat cockily on his head. Remember how he sauntered down the street, bell bottom trousers flapping from side to side? "I'll see you all before Christmas," he said. "It'll all be over by then." He only took one look back. Remember how his eyes smiled back at us as he turned that corner? We never saw him again.'

This was the first we'd heard about him. Although his photo took pride of place on the mantelpiece, this was the first time we boys had heard anything. I had never heard such a long speech from my Nan. I sensed foreboding permeating the kitchen

'Come on Mum, we'll help you.'

They all wiped their eyes as they went about

191

the preparations for the coming meal.

'Silly sod won't even go to the doctor.' She took her anger and frustration out on the potatoes, mashing them to a pulp.

When dinner was ready, Nan, Mum and Aunt Vera brought in the mounds of vegetables, steaming puddings and the small white enamel bucket used as a gravy boat, a large ladle sticking out of it. Everybody helped themselves. There was enough to satisfy the hungriest of mouths.

'I'll put Jack's dinner on a pot of boiling water with another plate over it,' said Aunt Vera. 'He can have it when he comes in from his shift.'

Nobody commented. The only sound was that of people munching. In between mouthfuls of food, Grumps burped his beer down.

'That was lovely, Rose,' he said, standing up. 'I think I'll go and have a lie down. What with the food and the fire, I'm feeling quite drowsy.'

'Not to mention the beer,' said Nan caustically.

'Now Rose, don't let's start.' He stretched his arms above his head, yawned and rubbed his chest. 'Bloody ticker's been acting funny lately.'

'Don't sleep too long, or you won't sleep tonight.'

'I know, I know. Just an hour will make a new man of me.'

I listened to his heavy boots clunking up the stairs.

'Anyone for tea?' said Nan. 'I'll make it. Who's doing the washing up?'

There was silence for a few seconds, us boys pretending we'd heard nothing.

'I suppose we will,' volunteered Mum and Aunt Vera.

We relaxed once more.

192

After the tea and the washing up, Dad turned on the wireless, waited two minutes for the valves in the set to warm up and then started turning the dial towards the Light Programme. Loud crackles escaped from the speaker before music suddenly blared out and the sparkly voice of Alma Cogan filled the room. *'The railroad comes through the middle of the house…'*

The front door creaked open, followed by a loud bang as it was shut. Jack opened the back room door. 'Blimey, it's parky out there.'

'Put the wood back in the hole, Jack. It's really draughty.'

'Sorry, Charlie.' Jack shut the door behind him and walked quickly over to the fire, rubbing his hands. 'Cor, it really is brass monkey weather out there.'

'Albert's upstairs having a kip. Hope that slamming door didn't wake him.'

'Wild elephants couldn't wake him, the amount of beer he's just tucked away,' said Nan.

'Charlie, go and wake Albert up will you? He's been asleep for two hours now; it's too long,' called Nan from the kitchen some time later.

Dad put down his paper and nodded. He disappeared through the door and up the stairs. A few moments later, his feet thumped quickly down again. 'Jack, can you come here?' He tried not to sound too anxious.

'What's up Charlie?'

'Just come here, will you?'

Minutes later, Uncle Jack and Dad walked back into the room and shut the door behind them.

'What's up Charlie?' asked Mum.

'Can't seem to wake Albert up,' he whispered. 'Jack, go round to the phone box by the offy and call an ambulance. Have you got tuppence?'

Jack jangled his pocket. Mum stood up.

'Why are you whispering?' I asked.

'Shush and play with your toys.' Dad placed his hands on Mum's shoulders, still whispering. 'Don't cry out now, I don't want to alarm Rose just yet. There's only one way to put this.' He looked around as if to make sure that none of us children could hear him, then looked Mum straight in the eye. 'I think your dad's gone.'

Gone where? I didn't hear him go out, I thought. I heard my mum echoing my thoughts.

'No Joyce, listen to me, I think he's gone.' Dad lifted his eyes to the ceiling. Mum stepped backwards, Dad just managing to keep hold of her. 'Jack's gone to call an ambulance. Please be quiet.'

Mum sat down in her chair. Tears began to trickle down her cheeks. With his body, Dad hid her from the rest of the family.

'Charlie, you want a cup of tea?' Nan shouted through the wall.

'No thanks, not just at the minute.'

Time dragged interminably, then the front door was heard to open. I heard Uncle Jack say, 'Upstairs, third door on the right.' He re-entered the back room, looking flushed. Two sets of footfall thundered up the stairs.

Nan walked into the back room looking straight at Dad. 'What's all that noise up there? Did you wake Albert? Where is he?'

Dad walked towards Nan, solemn faced. She spied Mum crying. Vera walked in from the kitchen. 'What's up Jack, you look really puffed?'

He just stood there, staring at Nan, who was slowly taking in the atmosphere.

'What's all that noise upstairs?' she repeated.

Us kids sat very still, staring silently at Dad reaching out to Nan. 'Rose, we had to call an ambulance. I couldn't wake Albert up. The men are up there now, looking at him.'

A great cry left her lips. Dad tried to restrain her but she brushed him aside. For all her bulk she rushed up the stairs two at a time.

'What's up?' asked Aunt Vera.

'I think your dad's gone.'

Vera stood with her arms hanging limply by her sides. She turned white and staggered. Catching herself in time, she held onto the door frame, mouth open, moaning softly. We heard a great scream coming from the top bedroom. June and Chris began to cry. Bob rushed out into the garden; he always wanted to be on his own in a crisis. I followed my dad up the stairs; nobody noticed me. We were just in time to see the ambulance men placing a sheet over Grumps' face. Nan stood at the bottom of the bed, rocking from side to side, biting on the tea towel she'd shoved into her mouth.

'Sorry, love, he must've gone peaceful like … never knew a thing, poor soul. We'll have to get him into the ambulance.'

One of the men left to get a stretcher. Dad turned and saw me as he put his arm round Nan, who stood trembling.

'What are you doing up here, boy! Go down stairs immediately!'

I ran down as fast as I could. Tears flowed freely down my cheeks. In less than twenty fours I'd cried too little for all that had happened.

'Come on Rose, we have to go downstairs. Let the men do their work.'

I watched him gently pushing Nan towards the door and guiding her down the stairs. The ambulance man stepped sideways past them, holding a wooden and canvas stretcher. I followed Dad and Nan into the warm back room.

'Sit down there, I'll make you a strong cup of tea.'

She sat down, staring into space, letting Dad take charge, the tea towel still in her mouth.

'You and the other kids will have to go to bed soon. Don't argue, just do as you're told. You'll have to sleep in the back room for a change.' Dad called Bob back inside and shepherded us all to the back bedroom. 'Now be good and go to sleep.' He quietly closed the bedroom door; the noise as the lock clicked shut seemed so final. All four of us cried and hugged each other to sleep.

The next morning Dad took me into the garden. Vera, Nan and Mum sat around the fire, eyes red with crying all night.

'Well Eric, I've something to tell you.' He stood there wringing his hands.

'Grumps is dead.'

Dad stared down at me. 'Yes, son, he is.'

'Can I go to the funeral?'

'No I'm afraid not, son; you're too young.'

'If I know he's dead, how does that make me too young?' I asked stubbornly.

'Now take my word for it: children are not allowed at funerals.' He held my shoulders firmly. Tears welled up in his eyes and he coughed loudly, wiping his eyes with the back of his hand. 'You and June have to stay with Mrs Smith for a few days. Be good and look after your sister. Bob and Chris are going to Aunt Maude's, the other side of London.'

I walked away from him, kicking the tufts of grass left by the scratching chickens. Involuntary tears ran down my cheeks. I stopped to stare at the chicken coops, the cat cages, the rabbits, which looked back at me through their wire mesh cages. Who would look after them now, with Grumps gone? No more arrowroot biscuits and ginger beer down at the pub, no more cat races. My tears flowed freely. I would miss him with my soul, my bones and my being.

Postscript

'The life of man is solitary, poor, nasty, brutish and short.'
— Thomas Hobbes 1588-1679

Life for us kids was hard and cruel, but with an underlying love which knew no bounds. The will to survive was ingrained in our very existence. We did not have time to feel sorry for ourselves. Everyday, we picked up the baton of life and carried on. Our families did their best with what they had. The laughter was pure. Men coming home from their labours, covered in soot, grime and grease, whistled down the street. Women, glued to kids and the kitchen sink, made the best of it.

I wouldn't swap my childhood for all the tea in China.

Acknowledgements

My grateful thanks go to Carol de Rose, a true friend who saw in me the potential skill to hone my words into a readable format.

Also to Frances Kavanagh and Jill Tipping, who kept the project alive with a mixture of tenacity, good humour, and patience.

And especially to my wife, Mary, who saw it through from beginning to the end with gentle cajoling and patience.

Last but not least, a book about any part of my life would not be complete without gratefully acknowledging the part played by my family, past and present friends, and passing ships in the night, some forever gone, some still whirring somewhere on this mortal coil, gone but never forgotten.

Eric Charles Bartholomew started writing when he was sixty years old (it's never too late), having worked in the city of London and abroad for over forty years, including five years lecturing in his chosen profession. The part he enjoyed the most was the travel. Luckily for him, his wife Mary also enjoys travel. Their first trip covered India, Sri Lanka and the Maldives. They fell in love with India and went back many times, eventually living there for several years. They have also travelled to Egypt, Africa, China, Outer Mongolia, Thailand, America, Europe and many other destinations, meeting wonderful fellow travellers, sharing their highs and lows, and swapping exaggerated stories over a glass or two of arak or feni.

Eric and Mary have been married for over forty years, and they have three children and two grandchildren. At present, they live in London, England.